Review,
Practice,
& Mastery of

Grade 4

D1378792

COMMON CORE
MATHEMATICS
STATE STANDARDS

Reviewers

Deanna Avery • Nantucket Public Schools • Nantucket, MA

Melinda Baer • Saddleback Valley Unified School District, Lake Forest, CA

Angela Kulacz • Elmhurst Unit School District • Elmhurst, IL

Debbie Smith • Opp City Schools • Opp, AL

© 2013 **Perfection Learning**®
www.perfectionlearning.com

1 2 3 4 5 6 EB 17 16 15 14 13 12

PP/Logan, Iowa, USA
04/13

94641
ISBN-10: 0-7891-8304-8
ISBN-13: 978-0-7891-8304-0

Printed in the United States of America.

To the Student

This book will help you review, practice, and master the Common Core State Standards for Mathematics. Here are the steps to follow to use this book.

1. Take the Tryout Test and check your answers. Use the chart at the bottom of this page to find out your strengths and weaknesses in the areas covered. Don't be discouraged if you don't get all the answers right or if you don't understand some questions. Remember the questions that are hard for you. They will be the types of questions you need to work on the most.

2. Work through the lessons that follow the Tryout Test. Each lesson reviews example items and provides a practice test based on the Common Core State Standards. Fill in the Keeping Score chart on page 109 as you complete each practice test.

3. After completing all the lessons, take the Mastery Test. Your score on this test will show your understanding of the Common Core State Standards for Mathematics.

Unit	Tryout Test Items	Mastery Test Items
1 Number Sense	1, 4, 7, 8, 10, 11, 14, 37	1, 4, 7, 8, 10, 11, 14, 37
2 Algebraic Thinking	2, 3, 5, 9, 22, 30, 32, 49	2, 3, 5, 9, 22, 30, 32, 49
3 Whole Number Operations	15, 16, 17, 19, 27, 39, 40, 42, 43	15, 16, 17, 19, 27, 39, 40, 42, 43
4 Fractions and Decimals	6, 12, 20, 21, 23, 24, 25, 26, 45, 46	6, 12, 20, 21, 23, 24, 25, 26, 45, 46
5 Measurement and Data	13, 28, 29, 38, 41, 44, 47, 50	13, 28, 29, 38, 41, 44, 47, 50
6 Geometry	18, 31, 33, 34, 35, 36, 48	18, 31, 33, 34, 35, 36, 48

Table of Contents

continued

Table of Contents *continued*

Tryout Test

Directions: Read each question and choose the best answer.

1 What is the value of 3 in 4,381,674?

Ⓐ *three hundred*

Ⓑ *three thousand*

Ⓒ *three hundred-thousand*

Ⓓ *three million*

2 What is the rule for this pattern?

2, 4, 8, 16, 32, . . .

Ⓐ Add 2.

Ⓑ Add 4.

Ⓒ Multiply by 2.

Ⓓ Multiply by 4.

3 What does x equal in this equation?

$$6 + x = 15$$

Ⓐ $x = 9$ Ⓒ $x = 21$

Ⓑ $x = 11$ Ⓓ $x = 23$

4 One year 426,071 people logged on to a Web site. Which answer shows 426,071 in word form?

Ⓐ *Four hundred twenty-six thousand, seven hundred one*

Ⓑ *Four hundred twenty-six thousand, seventy-one*

Ⓒ *Forty-two thousand, six hundred seventy-one*

Ⓓ *Four hundred twenty-six and seventy-one hundredths*

5 One week, Carlos ran 30 kilometers. That was 6 times as far as Aurora ran that week. Which equation can be used to find the number of kilometers Aurora ran?

Ⓐ $30 \times 6 = a$

Ⓑ $a + 6 = 30$

Ⓒ $6 \div a = 30$

Ⓓ $30 = 6 \times a$

6 Julie rides her bicycle $\frac{3}{10}$ miles each school day. How many miles does she ride in 5 days?

Ⓐ $\frac{15}{50}$ mi

Ⓑ $\frac{15}{30}$ mi

Ⓒ $\frac{15}{10}$ mi

Ⓓ $\frac{15}{5}$ mi

7 Which answer shows a factor pair for 64?

Ⓐ 3×22

Ⓑ 4×16

Ⓒ 6×12

Ⓓ 9×8

8 Charlie's favorite number is a prime number. Which could be his favorite number?

Ⓐ 16

Ⓑ 28

Ⓒ 33

Ⓓ 41

GO ON ⟹

9 Which shows the same type of pattern as the one below?

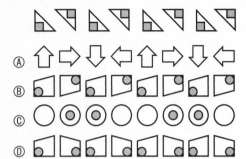

Ⓐ ⇧⇨⇩⇦⇧⇨⇩⇦

Ⓑ ▱▱▱▱▱▱▱▱

Ⓒ ○◎◉○○◎◉○

Ⓓ ▱▱▱▱▱▱▱▱

10 Prue's age is a multiple of 7. Which could be her age?

Ⓐ 26 years

Ⓑ 37 years

Ⓒ 42 years

Ⓓ 51 years

11 Which comparison is true?

Ⓐ 546,019 < 546,372

Ⓑ 279,511 < 278,064

Ⓒ 429,002 > 429,008

Ⓓ 162,426 > 162,822

12 How much farther is it to Rock than to Stone?

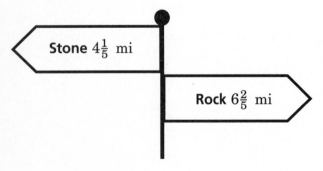

Ⓐ $1\frac{1}{5}$ mi

Ⓑ $2\frac{1}{5}$ mi

Ⓒ $2\frac{3}{5}$ mi

Ⓓ $10\frac{3}{5}$ mi

13 Ben wants to plant flowers around three sides of his shed. The area is shown by the shaded part of this diagram.

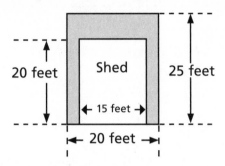

What area will he plant in flowers?

Ⓐ 300 square feet

Ⓑ 200 square feet

Ⓒ 125 square feet

Ⓓ 100 square feet

14 Which number rounded to the nearest hundred is NOT 2,400?

Ⓐ 2,368   Ⓒ 2,405

Ⓑ 2,390   Ⓓ 2,460

15 The towns of Mountainview and Valley View have populations of 38,754 and 62,041. To the nearest thousand, what is the BEST estimate of the difference in the towns' populations?

Ⓐ 30,000   Ⓒ 23,000

Ⓑ 24,000   Ⓓ 20,000

16 Becky made 4 batches of muffins. There are 24 muffins in each batch. She is going to put them into boxes that hold 10 muffins each. How many boxes, b, does she need.

Ⓐ $b = 5$

Ⓑ $b = 8$

Ⓒ $b = 9$

Ⓓ $b = 10$

17 One year Ms. Adams flew 24,377 miles. The next year she flew 31,408 miles. How many more miles did she fly the second year?

   Ⓐ 7,031 mi   Ⓒ 17,031 mi

   Ⓑ 7,131 mi   Ⓓ 55,785 mi

18 Wes drew a line and a ray. Which is his drawing?

Ⓐ 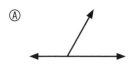   Ⓒ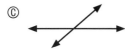

Ⓑ    Ⓓ

19 For which product is 2,500 a reasonable estimate?

   Ⓐ 210×8

   Ⓑ 88×62

   Ⓒ 47×52

   Ⓓ 38×38

20 Antoinetta ate $\frac{3}{8}$ of a pizza. Jacob ate $\frac{4}{8}$ of a pizza. What fraction of the pizza did they eat in all?

   Ⓐ $\frac{1}{8}$

   Ⓑ $\frac{7}{16}$

   Ⓒ $\frac{12}{64}$

   Ⓓ $\frac{7}{8}$

21 Which pair of fractions has a sum of $\frac{3}{7}$?

   Ⓐ $\frac{2}{7} + \frac{3}{7}$

   Ⓑ $\frac{1}{7} + \frac{2}{7}$

   Ⓒ $\frac{1}{7} + \frac{4}{7}$

   Ⓓ $\frac{2}{7} + \frac{2}{7}$

22 Leslie wrote the equation $42 = f \times 7$. Which problem could she have been solving?

   Ⓐ My cat eats 42 ounces of cat food a week. That is 7 times the amount she eats each day. How many ounces of cat food does she eat each day?

   Ⓑ My cat eats 42 ounces of cat food a week. How many ounces of cat food will she eat in 7 weeks?

   Ⓒ I bought 42 ounces of cat food. I fed my cat 7 ounces. How many ounces of cat food do I have left?

   Ⓓ I bought 42 ounces of cat food. I already had 7 ounces of cat food. How many ounces of cat food do I have in all?

23 Darla colored $\frac{8}{12}$ of the squares shown below.

Which fraction is equivalent to $\frac{8}{12}$?

   Ⓐ $\frac{2}{3}$ Ⓒ $\frac{1}{4}$

   Ⓑ $\frac{1}{2}$ Ⓓ $\frac{1}{16}$

24 Which sentence is true?

   Ⓐ $\frac{3}{5} > \frac{5}{10}$

   Ⓑ $\frac{1}{4} = \frac{4}{12}$

   Ⓒ $\frac{1}{3} < \frac{3}{12}$

   Ⓓ $\frac{6}{9} < \frac{2}{3}$

GO ON ⇨

25 Roger cut $\frac{6}{10}$ meters of rope. What is the decimal for the amount of rope he cut?

Ⓐ 0.006 meters

Ⓑ 0.06 meters

Ⓒ 0.6 meters

Ⓓ 6 meters

26 Which fraction is equal to $5\frac{1}{8}$?

Ⓐ $\frac{6}{8}$ Ⓒ $\frac{41}{8}$

Ⓑ $\frac{14}{8}$ Ⓓ $\frac{51}{8}$

27 Which of these number sentences is NOT true?

Ⓐ $5 \times (8 \times 3) = (5 \times 8) \times 3$

Ⓑ $5 \times 8 = 8 \times 5$

Ⓒ $5 \div 1 = 5$

Ⓓ $5 \div 0 = 5$

28 Juana measured her kitchen table. It was 6 feet long. How would she figure out how many yards long the table is?

Ⓐ Multiply 2 by 3.

Ⓑ Divide 6 by 3.

Ⓒ Multiply 2 by 12.

Ⓓ Divide 6 by 12.

29 These two rectangles have the same perimeter.

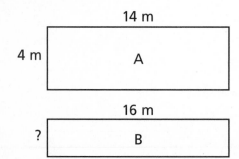

What is the width of rectangle B?

Ⓐ 2 m   Ⓒ 6 m

Ⓑ 4 m   Ⓓ 8 m

30 Chris can buy 3 tulip bulbs for $2. At this price, how much will 18 tulip bulbs cost?

Ⓐ $9   Ⓒ $18

Ⓑ $12   Ⓓ $27

31 Which figure has no line of symmetry?

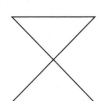

32 George had $48. He bought 2 pairs of gloves that cost $13 each. How much money did he have left after he bought the gloves?

Ⓐ $35   Ⓒ $22

Ⓑ $32   Ⓓ $15

33 Which of these is a right triangle?

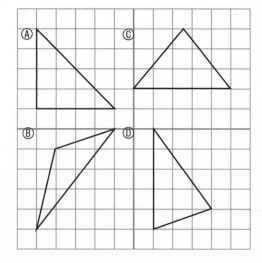

34 Which is true of both a rectangle and a parallelogram?

   Ⓐ Both have four right angles.

   Ⓑ Both have opposite sides parallel.

   Ⓒ Both have all right angles.

   Ⓓ Both have all sides the same length.

35 Which BEST describes two lines that are always the same distance apart?

   Ⓐ intersecting   Ⓒ parallel

   Ⓑ vertical   Ⓓ perpendicular

36 Which quadrilateral has four right angles?

   Ⓐ parallelogram   Ⓒ rhombus

   Ⓑ rectangle   Ⓓ trapezoid

Write an answer for each question.

37 Write 73,042 in expanded notation.

   Answer: _____

   _____

   _____

38 The line plot shows the heights of some pea plants after 3 weeks.

Heights of Pea Plants

```
                        X
        X           X   X
X       X           X   X
X       X       X   X   X
4¼     4½      4¾    5   5¼
```

Height (in Inches)

How much taller is the tallest plant than the shortest plant?

   Answer: _____

39 Robin asked 7 of her friends to help her write addresses on a batch of 1,256 envelopes. How many envelopes will each person address if they all address the same number?

   Answer: _____

40 What is the quotient?

$$600 \div 6 = \square$$

   Answer: _____

41 What is the measure of angle ADB?

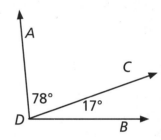

   Answer: _____

42 Stan paid $548 for his laptop. Marcie paid 3 times that amount for her laptop. How much did Marcie pay?

   Answer: _____

43 Grant uses 48 ounces of berries for every batch of jam he makes. How many ounces of berries does he need to make 26 batches of jam?

   Answer: _____

44 Angela has 17 pounds of ham. How many 6-ounce servings can she make? (Remember, there are 16 ounces in a pound.)

   Answer: _____

GO ON

45 Write an equivalent fraction for $\frac{9}{10}$ that has a denominator of 100.

Answer: _____

46 Jason earned \$67.75 last week. Carolyn earned \$67.90. Write <, >, or = to compare their earnings.

$67.75 \bigcirc $67.90

47 Sandy can ride her bicycle 16 miles in 1 hour. How far can she ride in $\frac{3}{4}$ of an hour?

Answer: _____

48 Classify the angles and identify perpendicular and parallel sides to describe this quadrilateral. Classify the quadrilateral.

Answer: _____

_____

_____

_____

_____

_____

49 Create a pattern that follows the rule *Subtract 5*.

Pattern: _____

Show all of your work. Explain in words the steps you follow.

Explanation:_____

_____

_____

_____

_____

_____

_____

_____

GO ON

50 Find the measures of ∠*ABC*, ∠CBD, and ∠ABD.

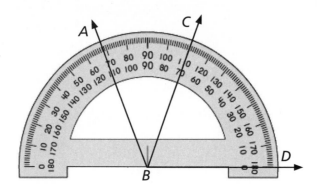

Answer: _____

Show OR describe each step of your work. Explain in writing each of your steps.

Explanation:_____

_____

_____

_____

_____

_____

Points Earned/Total = _____/50

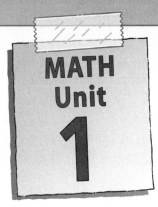

Number Sense

Directions: Read and answer each question.

Whole Number Place Value

1 What is the value of 5 in 5,236,879?

Ⓐ *five hundred*

Ⓑ *five thousand*

Ⓒ *five hundred-thousand*

Ⓓ *five million*

Remember . . .

Numbers are arranged in groups of three places, called a **period**. A comma separates the periods.

Step-By-Step

For **example 1** the value of the 5 is determined by its place in the number. Each place is 10 times the value of the place to its right.

1 Write the number in the place-value chart.

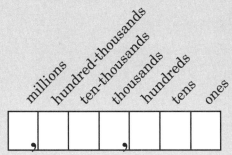

2 Find the 5. Read its value from the chart.

GO ON

2 What is the expanded notation for 430,573?

Ⓐ 400,000 + 30,000 + 500 + 70 + 3

Ⓑ 400,000 + 30,000 + 5,000 + 700 + 30

Ⓒ 400,000 + 3,000 + 500 + 70 + 3

Ⓓ 430,000 + 570 + 3

Expanded Notation

Expanded notation shows a number as the sum of the values of its digits.

5,303 = 5,000 + 300 + 3

Notice that values of zero are not included in expanded notation.

Step-By-Step

For **example 2**, find the value of each digit in 430,573. Then write the values as a sum.

1 Write the value of each digit.

4 hundred-thousands = 400,000

3 ten-thousands = 30,000

0 thousands = 0

5 hundreds = ☐

7 ☐ = ☐

3 ☐ = ☐

2 Write the non-zero values as a sum.

400,000 + 30,000 + 500 +

☐ + ☐

3 The population of a city is *five hundred four thousand, one hundred sixty-two.* Write this number in standard form.

Answer: _____

Ways to Express Numbers

Word form: *Seven hundred forty thousand, six hundred two*

Standard form: 740,602

Expanded form:
700,000 + 40,000 + 600 + 2

4 What is the word form for 8,130,237?

ⓐ *eight million, one hundred thirty thousand, three hundred twenty-seven*

ⓑ *eight million, one hundred three thousand, two hundred thirty-seven*

ⓒ *eight million, thirteen thousand, two hundred thirty-seven*

ⓓ *eight million, one hundred thirty thousand, two hundred thirty-seven*

Step-By-Step

Example 3 gives the number in word form. A place-value chart can help you write the number in standard form.

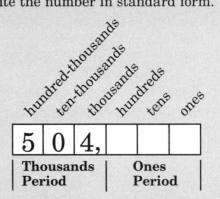

1 Read the number up to the word *thousand.*

five hundred four

2 Write the number 504 and a comma.

504,

3 Then read the rest of the number.

one hundred sixty-two

4 Write 162 to the right of the comma.

Think It Through

For **example 4**, write the number in a place-value chart. Use the words on the chart to help you choose your answer.

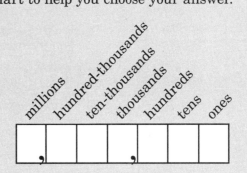

1 Which answer choice shows 3,456,037 written in word form?

Ⓐ *three million, four hundred fifty-six thousand, three hundred seven*

Ⓑ *three million, four hundred fifty thousand, six hundred thirty-seven*

Ⓒ *three million, four fifty-six thousand, thirty-seven*

Ⓓ *three million, four hundred fifty-six thousand, thirty-seven*

2 Write *nine hundred seven thousand, four hundred eight* in standard form.

Answer: _____

3 Write 37,423 in word form.

Answer: _____

4 Write the following number in standard form in the place-value chart.

four million, fifty-seven thousand, nine hundred thirteen

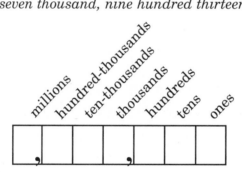

5 Write the following number in standard form in the place-value chart.

seventy thousand, nine hundred

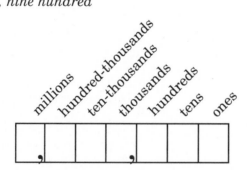

6 Write *six hundred fifty-seven thousand, two hundred eight* in standard form.

Answer: _____

5 Last week, there were 89,251 books on the shelves at the library. The week before, there were 89,387 books on the shelves. Which answer correctly compares the two numbers?

Ⓐ 89,251 < 89,387

Ⓑ 89,387 = 89,251

Ⓒ 89,251 > 89,387

Ⓓ 89,387 < 89,251

Remember . . .

Use these symbols to compare numbers.

< means *is less than.*

4 < 5

> means *is greater than.*

5 > 4

= means *is equal to.*

4 = 4

6 Which number makes the statement below true?

$$4{,}362{,}015 > \square$$

Ⓐ 4,350,000

Ⓑ 4,375,150

Ⓒ 4,440,703

D 5,001,999

Step-By-Step

To compare the numbers in **example 5**, line up their digits by place value. Then compare the digits from left to right.

1 Compare until you find digits that differ. The digits in the ten-thousands and thousands places are the same, so compare the hundreds.

89,251

89,387

2 The number 2 is less than 3, so 89,251 is less than 89,387.

89,**2**51

89,**3**87

3 Choose the answer that shows that 89,251 is less than 89,387.

Step-By-Step

You can read the statement for **example 6** as *4,362,015 is greater than what number?* You are looking for a number less than 4,362,015.

1 Start with the millions place. Eliminate answers with a number in the millions place greater than 4.

2 Eliminate answers with numbers in the hundred-thousands place greater than 3.

3 Continue comparing places to find the answer that is less than 4,362,015.

GO ON

7 Rewrite these numbers in order from least to greatest.

3,210,113   3,201,191
3,211,001

———   ———   ———

8 This series of numbers is in order from least to greatest. Write a number that can go in the blank.

450.99 _____ 451.01

9 Which has the greatest value?

Ⓐ 310.05   Ⓒ 311.5
Ⓑ 311.1   Ⓓ 310.95

10 Dan ran a race three times. Here are his times. Rewrite his times from least to greatest.

32.12   32.01   32.05

———   ———   ———

Rounding Whole Numbers

7 Round 349,217 to the nearest ten-thousand.

Answer: _____

Remember . . .

When you round up, → add 1 to the digit.

When you round down, → the digit stays the same.

Step-By-Step

For **example 7**, follow these steps.

1 Underline the number in the ten-thousands place. Then look at the digit to its right.

3 <u>4</u> 9, 2 1 7

2 If the number is less than 5, round down. If the number is greater than or equal to 5, round up.

9 is greater than 5, so round the ten-thousands digit up. 4 rounds up to 5.

3 5 ▯ , ▯ ▯ ▯

3 Change all of the digits after the ten-thousands place to zeros to finish writing the rounded number.

Rounding Whole Numbers

8 To the nearest hundred-thousand, the population of a city is 4,100,000. Which might be the population of the city?

Ⓐ 4,203,611

Ⓑ 4,187,302

Ⓒ 4,078,646

Ⓓ 4,032,065

Rounding Money

9 Last year, Ken earned $36,809. Which answer shows $36,809 rounded to the nearest thousand dollars?

Ⓐ $40,000   Ⓒ $36,000

Ⓑ $37,000   Ⓓ $36,800

Remember . . .

Round whole money amounts just like you would round whole numbers.

Think It Through

For **example 8**, you need to find the answer that can be rounded to 4,100,000.

Numbers between 4,050,000 and 4,149,999 round to 4,100,000. Which of the answers is between these two numbers?

Step-By-Step

For **example 9**, you are to round a money amount to the nearest thousand dollars.

1 Locate the thousands place.

$3 <u>6</u> , 8 0 9

2 Then look at the digit to the right of the thousands place.

$3 <u>6</u> , **8** 0 9

3 8 is greater than 5, so round up the digit in the thousands place. Change the rest of the digits to zeros.

$3 ☐ , ☐ ☐ ☐

10 Marsha ordered software for her new computer. The bill was $472.34. How much is $472.34 rounded to the nearest dollar?

Answer: _____

What About Cents?

When you round to the nearest dollar, the cents can be changed to zeros or you can write the dollar amount with no cents.

$85.71 rounds to $86.00 or $86.

Step-By-Step

To round to the nearest dollar in **example 10**, round to the ones place.

1 Locate the ones place.

$$\$4\ 7\ \underline{2}\ .\ 3\ 4$$

2 Look at the digit to the right of the ones place.

$$\$4\ 7\ \underline{2}\ .\ 3\ 4$$

3 The digit 3 is less than 5, so round down to the nearest dollar.

Round $472.34 to the nearest dollar.

$ [   ]

Try It

11 Round 675,291 to the nearest . . .

hundred: _____

thousand: _____

12 For your birthday, you receive $100.00 in ten-dollar and twenty-dollar bills. You take your birthday money to the mall. At the music store, you spend $44.05. How much money will you give the cashier?

Ⓐ $40.00   Ⓒ $50.00

Ⓑ $45.00   Ⓓ $60.00

13 Round 12.06 to the nearest . . .

whole number: _____

ten: _____

14 The six grandchildren in the Márquez family are 25, 22, 18, 17, 14, and 11 years old. Which of these ages round to 20 when rounded to the nearest ten?

Answer: _____

15 Which of the following numbers does NOT round to 34,500 when rounded to the nearest hundred?

Ⓐ 34,455

Ⓑ 34,550

Ⓒ 34,479

Ⓓ 34,542

16 Jessica is buying party hats. She needs 20. They come in packages of 6. How many packages should she buy?

Answer: _____

---

17 Round 2,346.2 to the nearest . . .

whole number: _____

ten: _____

hundred: _____

---

18 Ms. Chin removed $120.00 from the computer club account to spend on software. She got the money in $5, $10, and $20 bills. She spent $107.25 on software. How much did she give the cashier?

Ⓐ $100.00   C $110.00

B $105.00   D $120.00

Factors

11 What are all the factors of 27?

   Ⓐ 1, 3, 9

   Ⓑ 1, 3, 18, 27

   Ⓒ 1, 3, 9, 27

   Ⓓ 1, 27

Factor Pairs

Pairs of numbers that can be multiplied together to make a number are called *factor pairs*.

Factor pairs for 32 are:

32×1

16×2

8×4

You can use factor pairs to find all of the factors of a number.

Factors of 32: 1, 2, 4, 8, 16, 32

Step-By-Step

In **example 11**, a number is a factor of 27 if it divides into 27 with a remainder of 0.

1 You know that 27 is divisible by 1 and itself. Write these numbers in the box below.

2 Start at 2 and go through the numbers in your head. Ask yourself if 27 is divisible by each number.

Is 27 divisible by 2?

   No. 27 is not an even number.

Is 27 divisible by 3?

     Yes. $27 \div 3 = 9$

3 and 9 are both factors of 27. Write them in the box above.

3 Continue going through the numbers looking for factors of 27. When you get to 9, you can stop. You know that factors greater than 9 were found as factor pairs.

4 Choose the answer that shows all of the factors of 27.

GO ON

Prime and Composite Numbers

12 Which number between 20 and 28 is a prime number?

Answer: _____

Prime and Composite Numbers

A **prime number** has just 2 factors, 1 and itself.

A **composite number** has more than 2 factors.

Step-By-Step

For **example 12**, the answer choices are 20, 21, 22, 23, 24, 25, 26, 27, 28.

1 Eliminate all even numbers because they have 2 as a factor.

What numbers are left? _____

2 Eliminate all numbers that have 3 as a factor.

What numbers are left? _____

3 Find the factors of the two numbers. Which number has only 1 and itself as factors?

Factors of 23: _____

Factors of 25: _____

Multiples

13 Which choice lists the first ten multiples of 4?

Ⓐ 4, 8, 12, 16, 20, 22, 28, 32, 36, 40

Ⓑ 4, 8, 12, 16, 20, 24, 28, 32, 36, 40

Ⓒ 4, 8, 12, 14, 20, 24, 28, 32, 36, 40

Ⓓ 4, 8, 12, 16, 20, 24, 28, 32, 38, 40

Think It Through

To find multiples of 4 for **example 13**, multiply 4 by 1, 2, 3, 4, and so on. Then list the multiples in order. Complete the list of multiples below.

$4 \times 1 = 4$ $4 \times 6 =$ ____

$4 \times 2 = 8$ $4 \times 7 =$ ____

$4 \times 3 = 12$ $4 \times 8 =$ ____

$4 \times 4 = 16$ $4 \times 9 =$ ____

$4 \times 5 = 20$ $4 \times 10 =$ ____

Multiples

14 Which number is a multiple of 8?

Ⓐ 102

Ⓑ 96

Ⓒ 92

Ⓓ 86

Ways to Find Multiples

- **Skip count**.

Multiples of 5:   5, 10, 15, 20, 25, . . .

- **Multiply the number by 1, 2, 3, 4, and so on**.

Multiples of 9:   9, 18, 27, 36, . . .

9 × 1   9 × 2   9 × 3   9 × 4

Step-By-Step

One way to choose the correct answer for **example 14** is to compare the answers to multiples of 8.

1 You know that 10 × 8 = 80, and all of the answers are greater than 80, so multiply 11, 12, 13, and so on, by 8 to find multiples of 8.

11 × 8 = _____   12 × 8 = _____

13 × 8 = _____   14 × 8 = _____

2 Choose the answer that is a multiple of 8.

Another way is to divide each answer choice by 8. If the number is a multiple of 8, the remainder will be 0.

Try It

19 Which of these numbers is prime?

Ⓐ 15   Ⓒ 29

Ⓑ 21   Ⓓ 27

20 Which of the following sets of numbers includes only prime numbers?

Ⓐ 5, 7, 9   Ⓒ 13, 17, 21

Ⓑ 7, 11, 15   Ⓓ 17, 19, 24

21 Write all of the prime numbers between 10 and 20. (*Hint: there are 4 of them.*)

Answer: _____

22 Write the prime numbers greater than 1 and less than 12. (*Hint: there are 5 of them.*)

Answer: _____

23 Which of the following sets of numbers includes only composite numbers?

Ⓐ 2, 4, 6   Ⓒ 4, 6, 8

Ⓑ 3, 6, 9   Ⓓ 5, 7, 9

24 Which of these numbers is prime?

Ⓐ 21   Ⓒ 25

Ⓑ 23   Ⓓ 27

GO ON ⟶

25 Which of the following factor pairs are NOT factors of 20?

   Ⓐ 2, 8   Ⓒ 4, 5

   Ⓑ 2, 10   Ⓓ 1, 20

26 Find three different ways to write 16 as the product of two numbers.

   16 = _____ × _____

   16 = _____ × _____

   16 = _____ × _____

27 List all of the factors of 13.

   Answer: _____

28 Look at this list of factors for 20. Which number is missing?

   1, 2, 4, 10, 20

   Answer: _____

29 List all of the factors of 12.

   Answer: _____

30 Which of the following numbers is NOT a factor of 18?

   Ⓐ 2   Ⓒ 4

   Ⓑ 3   Ⓓ 6

31 What are 2 different ways to write 15 as the product of two numbers?

   15 = _____ × _____

   15 = _____ × _____

32 What do the numbers 3, 12, 15, and 21 all have in common?

   Ⓐ They are all prime numbers.

   Ⓑ They are all divisible by 3.

   Ⓒ They are all composite numbers.

   Ⓓ They all have a total of four factors.

33 Which set of numbers shows only multiples of 7?

   Ⓐ 28, 49, 64

   Ⓑ 42, 70, 84

   Ⓒ 1, 7, 49

   Ⓓ 14, 27, 56

34 Which of these is NOT a multiple of 9?

   Ⓐ 81

   Ⓑ 90

   Ⓒ 99

   Ⓓ 109

Go for it!

Test Practice 1: Number Sense

Estimated time: 20 minutes

Directions: Read and answer each question.

1 What is the standard form for *nine hundred two thousand, three hundred fifteen?*

Ⓐ 923,150

Ⓑ 920,315

Ⓒ 902,315

Ⓓ 92,315

2 What number is missing from this expanded notation?

$$36{,}245 = 30{,}000 + \underline{\quad} + 200 + 40 + 5$$

Ⓐ 6,000 Ⓒ 60

Ⓑ 600 Ⓓ 6

3 Which of the following numbers is NOT a factor of 18?

Ⓐ 2 Ⓒ 4

Ⓑ 3 Ⓓ 6

4 Which of these is a multiple of 3?

Ⓐ 23 Ⓒ 62

Ⓑ 41 Ⓓ 81

5 Connie paid $468.24 for a video camera. To the nearest ten dollars, how much did she pay for the camera?

Ⓐ $460

Ⓑ $468

Ⓒ $469

Ⓓ $470

6 The Amatos drove 1,326 kilometers during the first week of their vacation. They drove 1,529 kilometers during the second week. Which answer correctly compares the two distances?

Ⓐ $1{,}326 > 1{,}529$

Ⓑ $1{,}529 < 1{,}326$

Ⓒ $1{,}326 = 1{,}529$

Ⓓ $1{,}529 > 1{,}326$

7 Whose guess has 7 in the hundreds place?

Student Guesses for the Number of Beans in a Jar

Student	Guess
Emily	1,297
Rachel	5,688
Tory	5,753
Stephen	7,548

Ⓐ Emily's Ⓒ Tory's

Ⓑ Rachel's Ⓓ Stephen's

8 For the Fourth of July parade, the veterans used 17,212 flowers on their float. Which shows 17,212 in word form?

Ⓐ *seventeen and two hundred twelve*

Ⓑ *seventeen hundred thousand, two hundred twelve*

Ⓒ *ten thousand seven hundred twelve*

Ⓓ *seventeen thousand, two hundred twelve*

GO ON ⇨

9 Which set of numbers shows only multiples of 6?

Ⓐ 1, 6, 18   Ⓒ 2, 3, 6

Ⓑ 6, 18, 24   Ⓓ 6, 16, 26

10 Which answer shows a factor pair for 72?

Ⓐ 36 × 2   Ⓒ 9 × 7

Ⓑ 72 × 2   Ⓓ 18 × 3

11 Choose the number that is greater than 23,000 but less than 30,000.

Ⓐ 2,500   Ⓒ 25,000

Ⓑ 3,200   Ⓓ 32,000

12 What is the value of the underlined digit in 7,5̲38,492?

Ⓐ *five tens*

Ⓑ *five thousand*

Ⓒ *five hundred-thousand*

Ⓓ *five million*

13 A newspaper reported that 68,000 people attended a rally. The number is rounded to the nearest thousand. Which might be the number of people at the rally?

Ⓐ 72,466

Ⓑ 69,020

Ⓒ 68,841

Ⓓ 67,712

14 Which of these numbers is prime?

Ⓐ 15

Ⓑ 21

Ⓒ 33

Ⓓ 37

15 Which number correctly completes the statement below?

$$2,004,002 < \square$$

Ⓐ 1,948,306

Ⓑ 2,000,010

Ⓒ 2,003,668

Ⓓ 2,050,010

16 Which shows the expanded form for 50,601?

Ⓐ 50,000 + 6,000 + 100 + 1

Ⓑ 50,000 + 600 + 1

Ⓒ 5,000 + 600 + 10

Ⓓ 500 + 60 + 1

17 Which answer shows $47,472 rounded to the nearest thousand dollars?

Ⓐ $40,000   Ⓒ $48,000

Ⓑ $47,000   Ⓓ $50,000

18 Round 472,941 to the nearest ten thousand.

Answer: _____

19 List all of the factors of 8.

Answer: _____

20 There is only one even prime number. What is it?

Answer: _____

Number Correct/Total = _____/20

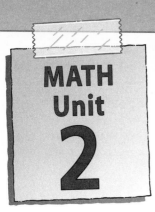

Algebraic Thinking

Directions: Read and answer each question.

Number Patterns

1 What are the next three numbers in this pattern?

3, 8, 7, 12, 11, 16, 15, 20, . . .

Ⓐ 25, 30, 35

Ⓑ 25, 24, 29

Ⓒ 19, 18, 17

Ⓓ 19, 24, 23

2 Amy made a pattern using the rule *multiply by 2*. Which pattern did she make?

Ⓐ 4; 8; 12; 16; 20; . . .

Ⓑ 4; 8; 16; 32; 64; . . .

Ⓒ 4; 6; 10; 16; 24; . . .

Ⓓ 4; 16; 64; 256; 1,024; . . .

Finding Change

Sometimes, more than one rule works for the first numbers in a pattern.

For example, a pattern that starts with 4, 8, . . . may use the rule *add 4* or the rule *multiply by 2*.

Be sure to check that the rule you choose works for ALL of the numbers in the pattern.

Think It Through

Look at the change from one number to the next to find the pattern for **example 1**.

$$3 \quad 8 \quad 7 \quad 12 \quad 11 \quad 16 \quad 15 \quad 20$$
$$+5 \quad -1 \quad +5 \quad -1 \quad +5 \quad -1 \quad +5$$

Continue the pattern to find the next three numbers.

Step-By-Step

For **example 2**, each number in the pattern is 2 times the number before it.

1 Look at the change from one number to the next for each answer.

Ⓐ 4; 8; 12; 16; 20
$$+4 \quad +4 \quad +4 \quad +4$$

Ⓑ 4; 8; 16; 32; 64
$$\times 2 \quad \times 2 \quad \times 2 \quad \times 2$$

Ⓒ 4; 6; 10; 16; 24
$$+2 \quad +4 \quad +6 \quad +8$$

Ⓓ 4; 16; 64; 256; 1,024
$$\times 4 \quad \times 4 \quad \times 4 \quad \times 4$$

2 Choose the pattern that was made using the rule *multiply by 2*.

GO ON ⇨

Shape Patterns

3 How many squares are needed to make the 8th figure in this pattern?

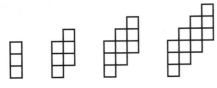

Fig 1   Fig 2   Fig 3   Fig 4

Ⓐ 3

Ⓑ 5

Ⓒ 15

Ⓓ 24

Tips

1 Listing data in a table can help you see the pattern.

2 When you identify a pattern, make sure it works for all of the pairs of numbers.

4 Alex says that the 111th figure in the example above has an odd number of squares. Which statement tells why?

Ⓐ The odd numbered figures have an odd number of squares.

Ⓑ The number of squares is twice the figure number.

Ⓒ The even numbered figures have odd numbers of squares.

Ⓓ The number of squares is the same as the figure number.

Step-By-Step

You can make a table to find the pattern for **example 3**.

1 List the number of squares for each figure.

Figure Number	Number of Squares
1	3
2	6
3	9
4	12
:	:
8	

2 Compare each pair of numbers. Look for an operation you can perform on the figure number to find the number of squares.

For the first figure:

$1 + 2 = 3$ *or* $1 \times 3 = 3$

3 Which operation, adding 2 or multiplying by 3, will work for the other pairs of numbers?

4 Use the operation *multiply by 3* to find the number of squares needed for Figure 8.

$8 \times 3 =$

Think It Through

For **example 4**, use the table to compare the figure numbers to the number of squares. Which statement is true?

5 Which shows the same type of pattern as the one below?

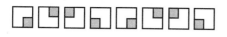

Ⓐ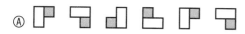

Ⓑ

Ⓒ

Ⓓ

Think It Through

Notice how the position of the square changes from one figure to the next in **example 5**.

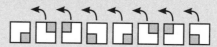

For each figure, the square is turned $\frac{1}{4}$ turn counterclockwise.

Look for the answer that shows $\frac{1}{4}$ turn counterclockwise from one figure to the next.

6 What rule can be used to find the number of squares needed to make the next figure in this pattern?

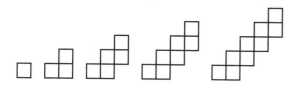

Ⓐ Add 2.
Ⓑ Add 3.
Ⓒ Multiply by 2.
Ⓓ Multiply by 3.

Step-By-Step

Use these steps to find the rule for **example 6**.

1 Find the number of blocks used to make each figure: 1, 3, 5, 7.

2 Find how the number of blocks changes from one figure to the next.

$$1, \quad 3, \quad 5, \quad 7$$
$$\backslash \; / \; \backslash \; / \; \backslash \; /$$
$$+2 \quad +2 \quad +2$$

3 Choose the rule that describes the pattern.

GO ON

1 Jared wrote the following number pattern. Which number comes next in his pattern?

4, 11, 18, 25, 32

Ⓐ 33
Ⓑ 36
Ⓒ 39
Ⓓ 41

2 Kathryn is recycling cans. During a break, she made the three stacks of cans shown below. How many cans will there be in Kathryn's fourth stack if she continues the pattern?

Answer: _____

3 Which number comes next in the number pattern?

32, 35, 38, 41, _____

Answer: _____

4 What rule will help you find the missing number?

44, 40, 36, 32, 28, _____

Ⓐ *Add 4*
Ⓑ *Divide by 4*
Ⓒ *Multiply by 4*
Ⓓ *Subtract 4*

5 Carla used this pattern to decorate a picture frame. What shape comes next in the pattern?

Ⓐ diamond
Ⓑ rectangle
Ⓒ star
Ⓓ triangle

Open-Ended Practice

Some tests include questions in which you must write an explanation of how you solved the problem. You may also be asked to show your work, draw graphs, or make diagrams. The example below will give you practice answering such questions.

Creating Patterns

7 Create a number pattern. Show at least five repetitions of your pattern.

Show OR describe each step of your work, even if you did it in your head ("mental math") or used a calculator.

Write an explanation stating the mathematical reason(s) why you chose each of your steps.

Answer: _____

Step-By-Step

When answering open-ended items, be sure to write clearly and label each step as in the example below.

My plan: *I will make up a rule and then use the rule to create the pattern.*

Step 1: The rule will have an operation and a number. I will use the rule *add 8*.

Step 2: I will start my pattern at 10. Then I will use the rule to create the pattern.

$$10, \quad 18, \quad 26, \quad 34, \quad 42, \quad 50, \quad 58$$
$$\backslash \;/\; \backslash \;/\; \backslash \;/\; \backslash \;/\; \backslash \;/\; \backslash \;/$$
$$+8 \quad +8 \quad +8 \quad +8 \quad +8 \quad +8$$

Explanation: *I made up the rule that was* add 8. *I decided to start my pattern at the number 10. I used the rule to create a pattern.*

Explanation: _____

_____

8 Grace had 4 carrot sticks in her lunch. After her friend Amy gave her some more carrot sticks, she had 11. How many carrot sticks did Amy give Grace?

Ⓐ 6

Ⓒ 8

Ⓑ 7

Ⓓ 9

Variables

A letter or symbol that stands for a number is called a *variable*.

Examples:

$\square + 3$ $\qquad$ $42 \div y$

Step-By-Step

To solve **example 8**, you can use a model.

1 Use 4 counters to represent the carrot sticks Grace had in her lunch.

2 Use a blank box to represent the number of carrot sticks Amy gave Grace.

3 Use 11 counters to represent the carrot sticks Grace had after receiving more from Amy.

$$\underset{\bigcirc\,\bigcirc}{\bigcirc\,\bigcirc} + \boxed{?} = \underset{\bigcirc\,\bigcirc\,\bigcirc\,\bigcirc\,\bigcirc}{\bigcirc\,\bigcirc\,\bigcirc\,\bigcirc\,\bigcirc\,\bigcirc}$$

4 How many counters do you need to place in the blank box to make the equation true?

9 Luke had 8 model dinosaurs. He got some more for his birthday. Now he has 13. How many model dinosaurs did he get for his birthday?

Answer: _____

Inverse Operations

Addition and subtraction are **inverse operations**. You can subtract to undo addition. You can add to undo subtraction.

$5 + 4 = 9$ $\quad$ $9 - 5 = 4$ $\quad$ $9 - 4 = 5$

$15 - 8 = 7$ $\quad$ $8 + 7 = 15$

Step-By-Step

For **example 9**, let d be the number of dinosaurs Luke got for his birthday.

1 Luke had 8 dinosaurs. He got d more. Now he has 13. The word *more* tells you the operation. Write the equation.

8 $\boxed{}$ $d = 13$

2 Rewrite the addition equation as a subtraction equation.

$8 + d = 13$

$d = 13 - \boxed{}$

3 Subtract to solve for d.

$d = \boxed{}$

4 Check by replacing your answer for d in the equation $8 + d = 13$.

6 A bean plant was 4 inches tall last month. It grew p inches this month. Now the plant is 25 inches tall Write an equation to fit the situation.

Answer: _____

7 Write an equation for this situation: Renaldo is playing a game. Renaldo has 3 points. Then he wins p more points. Now he has 5 points in all. (You don't have to solve the equation.)

Answer: _____

8 Which value makes the equation below true?

$$14 + b = 18$$

Ⓐ 2   Ⓒ 6
Ⓑ 4   Ⓓ 8

9 If $30 - v = 17$, what is the value of v?

Answer: _____

10 Jen has 18 books. She lends some to a friend. Now she has 11 books. Which equation shows how many books she lends to her friend?

Ⓐ $18 + b = 11$
Ⓑ $11 + 18 = b$
Ⓒ $b - 11 = 18$
Ⓓ $18 - b = 11$

11 Ming bought 5 baseball cards. Now he has 48 cards. How many did he have to begin with? Write a number sentence using c to represent the unknown number. Hint: there is more than one way to write the sentence!

Answer: _____

GO ON

10 Raul rode his bike 5 miles. To finish the race, he needs to ride 7 times that far. Which equation can be used to find the distance Raul needs to ride?

Ⓐ $5 \times 7 = d$

Ⓑ $5 + 7 = d$

Ⓒ $5 + d = 7$

Ⓓ $5 \times d = 7$

11 Ana's pumpkin has a mass of 54 kilograms. Omar's pumpkin has a mass of 9 kilograms. How many times greater is the mass of Ana's pumpkin?

Answer: _____

Inverse Operations

Remember that multiplication and division are **inverse operations**. You can multiply to undo division. You can divide to undo multiplication.

$4 \times 2 = 8$ $8 \div 2 = 4$ $8 \div 4 = 2$

$15 \div 3 = 5$ $5 \times 3 = 15$

Step-By-Step

For **example 10**, d stands for the distance Raul needs to ride.

1 Write the number of miles Raul rode.

2 Choose an operation. The word *times* tells you the operation.

5

3 Write the number of times as far Raul needs to ride.

5 ×

4 Complete the equation by writing the equal sign and the variable for the distance Raul needs to ride. Then choose the answer that matches your equation.

For **example 11**, the words *how many times* tells you that you can write a multiplication equation for the problem.

1 The mass of Omar's pumpkin times some number equals the mass of Ana's pumpkin. Let n be the number. Write an equation.

× n =

2 Rewrite the multiplication equation as a division equation.

$9 \times n = 54$

$n = 54 \div$

3 Solve for n.

$n =$

4 Check by replacing your answer for n in the equation $9 \times n = 54$.

12 Ms. Sanchez has 30 oranges to give to her students. She has 15 students. Which equation can be used to find n, the number of oranges each student will get?

    Ⓐ $n = 15 \times 30$

    Ⓑ $n = 30 \div 15$

    Ⓒ $n \times 30 = 15$

    Ⓓ $15 \div n = 30$

13 In the number sentence $4 \times \boxed{} = 36$, what number goes in the box?

    Ⓐ 6   Ⓒ 12

    Ⓑ 9   Ⓓ 18

14 Letti brings 6 tennis balls to the court. Maria brings t tennis balls. In all, they have fewer than 12 tennis balls. Which inequality fits this situation?

    Ⓐ $6 + t = 12$

    Ⓑ $12 - t = 12$

    Ⓒ $12 > 6 - t$

    Ⓓ $6 + t < 12$

15 Drew wrote the following equation:

$$4 \times n = 36$$

Which problem could he have been solving?

    Ⓐ A family paid $36 dollars to rent a paddle boat for 4 hours. What was the cost of the paddle boat for 1 hour?

    Ⓑ Camille found 36 coins when cleaning her desk and 4 more coins under the bed. How many coins did she find in all?

    Ⓒ There are 36 cookies to be divided equally into 9 plastic bags. How many cookies go into each bag?

    Ⓓ The original price of a radio is $36. The radio is on sale for $4 less. What was the sale price of the radio?

16 Which expression means "55 divided by a number (n)"?

    Ⓐ $55 \div n$ Ⓑ $55 + n$

    Ⓒ $n - 5$ Ⓓ $55 \times n$

GO ON

Multistep Equations

12 The table compares Ming's steps with her baby sister's steps.

Number of Steps	Baby's Distance (in inches)	Ming's Distance (in inches)
1	5	20
2	10	40
3	15	60
4	20	80

Each girl took the same number of steps. If the baby walks 40 inches, how far will Ming walk?

Ⓐ 120 inches

Ⓑ 160 inches

Ⓒ 200 inches

Ⓓ 240 inches

Step-By-Step

For **example 12**, let s stand for the number of steps.

1 Find the rule for the number of inches the baby travels with each step. Write the rule as an expression.

Multiply steps by ☐.

$s \times$ ☐

2 Use the expression to find the number of steps it takes the baby to walk 40 inches. Think: What number times 5 equals 40?

☐ $\times 5 = 40$

3 Find the rule and write an expression for the number of inches Ming travels in each step.

Multiply steps by ☐.

$s \times$ ☐

4 Use the expression to find the number of inches Ming traveled in 8 steps.

$8 \times 20 =$ ☐

13 Hannah bought 7 boxes of wheels. There are 4 wheels in each box. She is using the wheels to make tricycles. How many tricycles can she make?

Show OR describe each step of your work, even if you did it in your head ("mental math") or used a calculator. Write your answer on the line.

Write an explanation stating the mathematical reason(s) why you chose each of your steps.

Answer: _____

Explanation: _____

_____

_____

_____

_____

_____

Step-By-Step

When solving open-ended problems, be sure to write clearly and label each step.

My Plan

First, I need to find the number of wheels Hannah bought. Then I need to find the number of tricycles Hannah can make. I will write equations, letting w be the number of wheels and t be the number of tricycles.

Step 1 To find the total number of wheels, w, I can multiply the number of boxes of wheels, 7, by the number of wheels in each box, 4.

$$w = 7 \times 4$$

$$w = 28 \text{ wheels}$$

Step 2 Each tricycle Hannah makes will have 3 wheels. To find the number of tricycles, t, I will divide the 28 wheels by 3.

$$t = 28 \div 3$$

$$t = 9 \text{ R1}$$

The quotient is the number of tricycles Hannah can make, 9. The remainder is the number of wheels she will have left over, 1.

Step 3 I need to check that the answer is correct. I can use mental math and work backward.

3 wheels $\times$ 9 tricycles + 1 wheel = 28 wheels

28 wheels $\div$ 4 wheels in a box = 7 boxes
It checks.

17 Carter got $45 on his birthday. After paying back his sister $10, he spent $15 on a DVD. Then he put half of what was left in the bank. How much money does he have left to spend?

Ⓐ $35

Ⓑ $20

Ⓒ $10

Ⓓ $5

18 Mario had 12 pet fish in his fish tank. He bought 2 more fish. Then he bought a second fish tank. He divided his fish evenly into the two tanks. How many fish are in each tank?

Answer: _____

19 Lucy's hair is 30 centimeters long. Amy's hair is 12 centimeters shorter. Jenny's hair is 5 centimeters longer than Amy's. How long is Jenny's hair?

Answer: _____ centimeters

20 Myrna bought 6 pizzas. Each pizza had 8 slices. She saved two pizzas for her brothers, then divided the rest equally between herself and 7 friends. How many slices did Myrna and each of her friends get?

Ⓐ 6

Ⓑ 5

Ⓒ 4

Ⓓ 3

Go for it!

Test Practice 2: Algebraic Thinking

Estimated time: 25 minutes

Directions: Read and answer each question.

1 What is the missing number in this pattern?

$$62, 59, 56, \underline{\quad}, 50, 47, 44, \ldots$$

Ⓐ 55 Ⓒ 52

Ⓑ 53 Ⓓ 51

2 Which equation can be used to answer this question?

There are 24 candy bars in a bag. Leon already took 9 candy bars. How many more candy bars are left in the bag?

Ⓐ $24 - 9 = \underline{\quad}$

Ⓑ $24 + 9 = \underline{\quad}$

Ⓒ $24 + \underline{\quad} = 9$

Ⓓ $9 \times \underline{\quad} = 24$

3 Shona worked 16 hours last week. Melanie worked 3 times that many hours. Which equation can be used to find the number of hours Melanie worked?

Ⓐ $16 \times 3 = h$

Ⓑ $h + 3 = 16$

Ⓒ $16 \div 3 = h$

Ⓓ $3 = 16 - h$

4 Julio created a pattern using the rule *subtract 5*. Which pattern did he make?

Ⓐ $52, 47, 42, 37, 32, \ldots$

Ⓑ $52, 47, 40, 31, 20, \ldots$

Ⓒ $52, 57, 62, 67, 72, \ldots$

Ⓓ $52, 57, 63, 70, 78, \ldots$

5 Mrs. Cardillo made 24 pancakes. Her family ate p pancakes. Now only 8 pancakes are left.

Which equation describes this situation?

Ⓐ $24 + p = 8$ Ⓒ $24 - p = 8$

Ⓑ $24 \div p = 8$ Ⓓ $24 \times 8 = p$

6 Keenan collects 3 shells for every 5 shells Deon collects. How many shells will Keenan have when Deon has 45?

Ⓐ 9 Ⓒ 27

Ⓑ 15 Ⓓ 135

7 Victor started at 15 and used the rule *add 15* to make a pattern. What are the first three numbers in the pattern?

Answer: _____

8 Kea has 8 shelves of CDs. There are 9 CDs on each shelf. She is packing the CDs into boxes that hold 10 CDs each. How many boxes does she need?

Answer: _____

9 Denzel used a rule to make this pattern.

$$67, 63, 59, 55, 51, \ldots$$

Which of these patterns uses the same rule?

Ⓐ $16, 21, 26, 31, 36$

Ⓑ $80, 75, 70, 65, 60$

Ⓒ $88, 84, 80, 76, 72$

Ⓓ $76, 71, 67, 64, 62$

GO ON

10 Will the 10th figure in this pattern have an even or an odd number of squares?

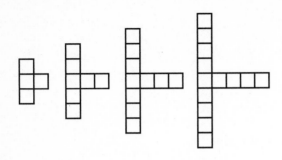

Answer: _____

11 What is the next figure in this pattern?

 **?**

Ⓐ ⇦

Ⓑ ⇧

Ⓒ ⇨

Ⓓ ⇩

12 Which shows the same type of pattern as the one below?

Ⓐ ☆○♡☆○♡☆○♡

Ⓑ ♡☆☆○♡☆☆○♡☆☆○♡☆☆○

Ⓒ ○☆○♡○☆○♡○☆○♡○☆○♡

Ⓓ ☆○♡♡♡○☆○♡♡♡○☆○♡♡○

13 Which rule can you use to find the number of triangles needed to make the next figure in this pattern?

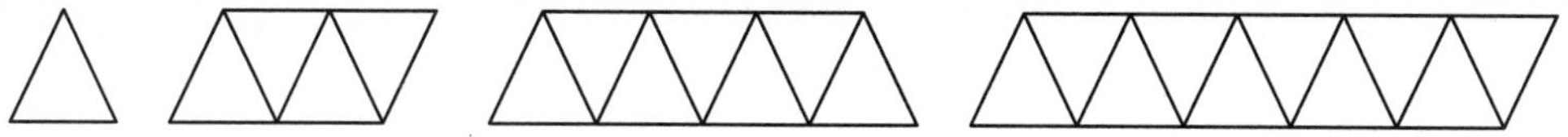

Ⓐ *Add 2* Ⓒ *Add 5*
Ⓑ *Add 3* Ⓓ *Multiply by 3*

14 Write a story that matches this equation. Then solve the equation.

$$5 \times p = \$60$$

Story: _____

_____

_____

Show OR describe each step of your work, even if you do it in your head ("mental math") or use a calculator. Explain in writing why you chose each of your steps.

Answer: _____

Explanation: _____

_____

_____

_____

STOP

Points Earned/Total = _____ /14

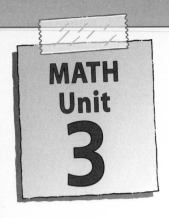

MATH Unit 3

Whole Number Operations

1 Estimating Sums and Differences [**4.OA.3**]
2 Adding and Subtracting Whole Numbers [**4.NBT.4**]
3 Estimating Products and Quotients [**4.OA.3**]
4 Properties of Operations [**4.NBT.5**] [**4.NBT.6**]
5 Using Basic Facts and Place Value to Multiply and Divide [**4.NBT.1**] [**4.NBT.2**] [**4.NBT.3**]
6 Multiplying by One-Digit Numbers [**4.NBT.5**]
7 Multiplying by Two-Digit Numbers [**4.NBT.5**]
8 Dividing Whole Numbers [**4.NBT.6**]
9 Interpreting Remainders [**4.OA.3**] [**4.NBT.6**]

Directions: Read and answer each question.

Estimating Sums and Differences

1 One month, 34,295 people rode the city bus. The next month, 48,377 people rode the bus. About how many people rode the city bus during these two months?

Ⓐ 60,000
Ⓑ 70,000
Ⓒ 80,000
Ⓓ 90,000

When to Estimate

Estimate when you do not need an exact answer.

Estimate when you need to know "about how much."

Estimate to check that calculations are reasonable.

Step-By-Step

To estimate the total number of visitors for **example 1**, round each number to the nearest ten-thousand.

1 Round 34,295 to the ten-thousands place. The thousands digit is 4, so round down.

$\underline{3}4,295$ rounds to 30,000.

2 Round 48,377 to the ten-thousands place. The thousands digit is 8, so round up.

$\underline{4}8,377$ rounds to ⬜ .

3 Add the rounded numbers.

$$\begin{array}{r} 30,000 \\ +\ \underline{50,000} \\ \hline \end{array}$$

© **Perfection Learning**® **No reproduction permitted.**

Estimating Sums and Differences

2 This table shows the number of ride tickets sold at the Fun Day Amusement Park in May and June.

Month	Tickets
May	46,896
June	61,347

About how many more tickets were sold in June than in May? Estimate by rounding the numbers to the nearest thousand before finding the difference.

Ⓐ 13,000

Ⓑ 14,000

Ⓒ 15,000

Ⓓ 16,000

Step-By-Step

For **example 2**, round the numbers to the nearest thousand. Then subtract.

1 46,896 rounds up to ⬚ .

2 61,347 rounds down to ⬚ .

3 Subtract the rounded numbers.

$$\begin{array}{r} 61,000 \\ -\ 47,000 \\ \hline \end{array}$$

Try It

1 Which is a good estimate of the difference?

$$651 - 302$$

Ⓐ 300   Ⓒ 400

Ⓑ 350   Ⓓ 950

2 Two schools have recycling programs. One school recycled 3,471 cans during a month. Another school recycled 672 cans. About how many cans did both schools recycle all together?

Ⓐ 2,000   Ⓒ 4,200

Ⓑ 3,500   Ⓓ 9,000

3 Which is a good estimate of the sum?

$$0.75 + 2.3$$

Ⓐ 1   Ⓒ 5

Ⓑ 3   Ⓓ 10

4 Danville has a population 3,412. The neighboring town of Jackson has a population of 1,566. About how many more people live in Danville than in Jackson? Estimate to the hundreds place.

Answer: _____

GO ON

3 Two fourth-grade classes have a goal of
collecting 1,000 pounds of newspaper for a
paper drive. So far, one class has collected
386 pounds of newspaper. The other class
has collected 428 pounds. How many more
pounds of newspaper do the two classes
need to collect to make their goal?

Ⓐ 296 pounds

Ⓑ 286 pounds

Ⓒ 186 pounds

Ⓓ 162 pounds

Regrouping in Addition

When you add, remember to write
down the regrouped numbers.

Think: 9 + 4 = 13.

Write a 3 in the ones place in the
sum. Write a 1 above the tens place.

$$\begin{array}{r} 1 \\ 219 \\ +\ 54 \\ \hline 3 \end{array}$$

Regrouping in Subtraction

When you subtract, remember to
write down the regrouped numbers.

Think: I cannot subtract 8 from 7.
Rewrite 5 tens and 7 ones as 4 tens
and 17 ones.

$$\begin{array}{r} 4\ 17 \\ 6\cancel{5}\cancel{7} \\ -\ 48 \end{array}$$

Step-By-Step

To solve **example 3**, find the total number
of pounds of newspaper collected so far.
Then subtract to find how many more
pounds are needed to make the goal.

1 Add to find the total pounds of
newspapers collected by the two classes.
Write the addition in vertical form.
Align the digits by place value and
add from right to left. Regroup when
necessary.

$$\begin{array}{r} 1\ 1 \\ 386 \\ +\ 428 \\ \hline 814 \end{array}$$

2 Subtract the total from 1,000. You will
have to rename 1,000 as 9 hundreds,
9 tens, and 10 ones before you can
subtract.

$$\begin{array}{r} 9\ 9\ 10 \\ 1,\cancel{0}\cancel{0}\cancel{0} \\ -\ 8\ 1\ 4 \\ \hline 8\ 6 \end{array}$$

3 Complete the subtraction to answer the
question.

5 The Clive Music Center has two concert halls. Mark Hall seats 348 people. Lang Hall has 905 seats. How many seats is that combined?

Answer: _____

6 Find the sum of 567 and 35.

ⓐ 592   © 567

Ⓑ 602   Ⓓ 56,735

7 Find the difference between 1,303 and 279.

Answer: _____

Estimating Products and Quotients

4 Mike used a calculator to multiply 58×39. The display on the calculator showed 3,315. Which of the following is a true statement?

ⓐ 3,315 a reasonable answer.

Ⓑ 3,315 is less than the actual answer.

© The actual answer should be between 1,500 and 2,400.

Ⓓ The actual answer is greater than 3,315.

Step-By-Step

For **example 4**, you can use estimation to check the reasonableness of the answer.

1 Round both the factors to *greater* numbers to get an **overestimate**.

58 rounds up to   60
39 rounds up to   × 40

multiply: ▢

2 Round both the factors to *lesser* numbers to get an **underestimate**.

58 rounds down to   50
39 rounds down to   × 30

multiply: ▢

3 The actual product will be a number between the overestimate and the underestimate.

GO ON ⇨

5 Seven friends collected 368 pounds of paper to recycle. Each collected about the same number of pounds. About how many pounds of paper did each collect?

Ⓐ 20

Ⓑ 50

Ⓒ 80

Ⓓ 100

Think It Through

Example 5 asks *about* how many pounds each person collected, so you can estimate. You are dividing by 7, so think of a number close to 368 that is easy to divide by 7.

Use the fact 35 ÷ 7 = 5.

350 ÷ 7 = ☐

Compatible Numbers

Easy-to-calculate numbers that are close to the original numbers are called *compatible numbers*.

Try It

8 Estimate: 646 ÷ 8

Ⓐ 8   Ⓒ 800

Ⓑ 80   Ⓒ 808

9 Sebastian is building a block wall. The wall will be 48 blocks long and 5 blocks tall. About how many blocks does he need?

Ⓐ 55   Ⓒ 250

Ⓑ 200   Ⓓ 500

10 Jessie wants to plant 8 rows of tulip bulbs with 38 bulbs in each row. Which is the BEST estimate of the number of tulip bulbs he needs?

Ⓐ 50   Ⓒ 320

Ⓑ 240   Ⓓ 400

6 The expression $(5 \times 4) + (5 \times 3)$ can be used to find the area of this figure.

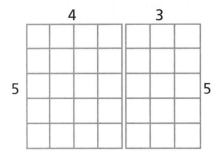

Which answer is another expression for finding the area?

Ⓐ $(5 + 4) \times (5 + 3)$

Ⓑ $(5 \times 5) + (4 + 3)$

Ⓒ $5 + (4 \times 3)$

Ⓓ $5 \times (4 + 3)$

7 What is 67×7?

Ⓐ 409

Ⓑ 429

Ⓒ 449

Ⓓ 469

Distributive Property

The product of a sum or difference equals the sum or difference of two products.

$$3 \times (4 + 6) = 3 \times 4 + 3 \times 6$$

$$5 \times (8 - 2) = 5 \times 8 - 5 \times 2$$

Think It Through

The area of the figure in **example 6** is expressed as the sum of the areas of two rectangles: one rectangle 5 units long by 4 units wide and the other 5 units long by 3 units wide.

$$(5 \times 4) + (5 \times 3)$$

Think of the figure as a single rectangle that is 5 units long by $(4 + 3)$ units wide. The area is the product of *5 times the sum of 4 + 3*. Choose the expression that can be used to find the area.

Step-By-Step

To answer **example 7**, you can use the Distributive Property of Multiplication. This property states that to multiply a sum by a number, multiply each addend by the number and add the products.

1 Rewrite the problem, writing 67 as the sum of two addends.

$$67 \times 7 = (60 \times 7) + (7 \times 7)$$

2 Multiply each pair of factors.

$$(60 \times 7) + (7 \times 7)$$

$$\boxed{} + \boxed{}$$

3 Add the factors.

Properties of Operations

8 Which property is shown by the number sentence below?

$$(2 \times 8) \times 5 = 2 \times (8 \times 5)$$

Ⓐ Commutative Property

Ⓑ Associative Property

Ⓒ Distributive Property

Ⓓ Zero Property

Properties of Operations

Commutative Property	The **order** in which you *add* or *multiply* numbers does not change the answer.	$2 \times 6 = 6 \times 2$ $3 + 5 = 5 + 3$
Identity Property of Multiplication	The product of any number and **1** is that same number.	$2 \times 1 = 2$
Identity Property of Addition	The sum of any number and **0** is that same number.	$2 + 0 = 2$
Associative Property	You can change the **grouping** of *addends* or *factors* and the sum or product will be the same.	$(4 + 2) + 3 = 4 + (2 + 3)$ $(2 \times 3) \times 4 = 2 \times (3 \times 4)$
Zero Property of Multiplication	When you multiply a number and 0, the product is 0.	$0 \times 7 = 0$ $45 \times 0 = 0$

11 Is this statement true or false? Which property does the statement show?

$$64 \times 1 = 64$$

True or False? _____

Property: _____

12 Is this statement true or false? Which property does the statement show?

$$15 + 0 = 15$$

True or False? _____

Property: _____

13 Which property is shown by the number sentence below?

$$6 \times (5 + 4) = (6 \times 5) + (6 \times 4)$$

Ⓐ Commutative Property
Ⓑ Associative Property
Ⓒ Distributive Property
Ⓓ Zero Property

Using Basic Facts and Place Value to Multiply and Divide

9 What is the product?

$$40 \times 200$$

Ⓐ 80,000   Ⓒ 800

Ⓑ 8,000   Ⓓ 80

Remember . . .

You can use multiplication facts and place value to multiply multiples of ten.

60	Think: 6 tens
× 7	× 7
	42 tens = 420

Step-By-Step

For **example 9**, you can use the basic multiplication fact 4×2. Then count the zeros in the factors to find the product.

1 Find the product for the basic fact.

$$4 \times 2 = \boxed{}$$

2 Count the number of zeros in each factor.

$$40 \times 200$$

There are $\boxed{}$ zeros.

3 Write three zeros after the product.

8, $\boxed{}$ $\boxed{}$ $\boxed{}$

GO ON →

10 Divide.

$$350 \div 50$$

Ⓐ 7   Ⓒ 1,750

Ⓑ 70   Ⓓ 17,500

Why Can You Delete the Zeros?

You are dividing both the divisor and the dividend by 10 when you delete the zeros in example 10. Then you can divide 35 by 5 rather than dividing 35 tens by 5 tens.

Multiplying by One-Digit Numbers

11 Airplane tickets cost $329 each. How much will tickets for a family of 4 cost?

Answer: _____

Step-By-Step

To answer **example 10**, you can delete zeros to make the problem easier to solve.

1 Cross off the same number of zeros in both the dividend and the divisor.

$$35\not{0} \div 5\not{0} = 35 \div 5$$

2 Think: 5 times what number equals 35?

$$5 \times \boxed{} = 35$$

3 That number is the quotient for the division problem.

$$350 \div 50 = \boxed{}$$

Step-By-Step

For **example 11**, multiply to find the cost of 4 airplane tickets.

1 Write the multiplication problem vertically. Multiply the ones place digit first: $4 \times 9 = 36$. Write the 6 in ones place in the product. Regroup 30 ones as 3 tens.

$$\begin{array}{r} 3 \\ 329 \\ \times\ 4 \\ \hline 6 \end{array}$$

2 Multiply the tens. 4×2. Add the 3. Write 1 in tens place in the product. Regroup the 10 tens as 1 hundred.

$$\begin{array}{r} 1\ 3 \\ 329 \\ \times\ 4 \\ \hline 16 \end{array}$$

3 Multiply the hundreds. 4×3. Add the 1. Don't forget the dollar sign.

$$\begin{array}{r} 1\ 3 \\ 329 \\ \times\ 4 \\ \hline \boxed{}16 \end{array}$$

Multiplying by Two-Digit Numbers

12 Hannah bought 13 boxes of oranges. Each box contained 28 oranges. How many oranges did she buy in all?

Ⓐ 84

Ⓑ 264

Ⓒ 364

Ⓓ 384

Simplifying

You can break multiplication problems into simpler parts. Look at the simplified solution to this problem.

$$28 \times 36 =$$

$20 \times 30 =$	600
$20 \times 6 =$	120
$8 \times 30 =$	240
$8 \times 6 =$	48
Add:	1,008

$$28 \times 36 = 1,008$$

Step-By-Step

For **example 12**, you will need to multiply two two-digit numbers.

1 You know the number of boxes (13) and the number of oranges in each box (28). To find the total, multiply the number of oranges in each box by the number of boxes.

2 It is usually easier to write the smaller number below the larger number. Multiply 3 times 28, multiply 10 times 28, and then add.

$$\begin{array}{r} 28 \\ \times\ 13 \\ \hline 84 \\ +\ 280 \\ \hline \end{array}$$

Try It

14 Use mental math to solve this problem.

$$23 \times 3,000 =$$

Answer: _____

15 $912 \times 33 =$

Ⓐ 2,736

Ⓑ 5,472

Ⓒ 27,360

Ⓓ 30,096

GO ON

16 The Pine Island Ferry can hold 185 passengers. It makes 12 one-way trips per day. How many passengers will it carry in one day if all of the trips are full? Show your work in the space below. Then write your answer on the line.

Answer: _____ passengers

17 For Arbor Day, 45 different ecology clubs raised $250 each to pay for new tree plantings. How much money did they raise in all? Show your work in the space below. Then write your answer on the line.

Answer: _____

18   465
       $\times\ 95$

Answer: _____

19 $42 \times 66 =$

Answer: _____

20 $755 \times 91 =$

Ⓐ 687,050   Ⓒ 67,950

Ⓑ 68,705   Ⓓ 7,550

21 What is the product?

$$60 \times 600$$

Ⓐ 36   Ⓒ 3,600

Ⓑ 360   Ⓓ 36,000

22 Divide.

$$600 \div 60$$

Answer: _____

23 E-book readers cost $179. How much will e-book readers cost for a family of 6?

Answer: _____

Dividing Whole Numbers

13 Kan and Wei went to dinner. The check totaled $76. They decided to share the cost equally. How much money did each pay?

Ⓐ $33

Ⓑ $38

Ⓒ $43

Ⓓ $48

Dividing Larger Numbers

To divide larger numbers repeat these steps.

1 Divide

2 Subtract

3 Bring down

Step-By-Step

For **example 13**, you need to divide.

1 Rewrite the problem and divide the tens.

$$\begin{array}{r} 3 \\ 2\overline{)76} \\ -6 \end{array}$$ *Multiply 2 × 3.*

2 Subtract the tens.

$$\begin{array}{r} 3 \\ 2\overline{)76} \\ -6 \\ \hline \end{array}$$

3 Bring down the 6 ones and divide the ones.

$$\begin{array}{r} 38 \\ 2\overline{)76} \\ -6 \\ \hline 16 \\ -16 \\ \hline \end{array}$$

Showing Division

You can use place-value blocks to model division.

$$76 \div 2 = 38$$

| 76 = 7 tens and 6 ones | Divide the tens by 2 | Regroup 1 ten as 10 ones | Divide the 16 ones by 2 |

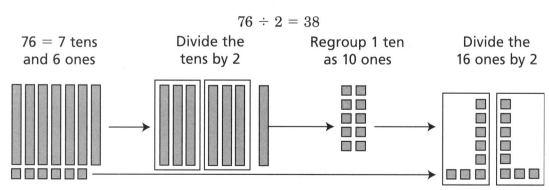

GO ON

14 There are 4 bottles of juice in a carton. Cheyenne needs 58 bottles of juice for her class. How many cartons should she buy? (Cheyenne must purchase only complete cartons.)

Ⓐ 22

Ⓑ 15

Ⓒ 14

Ⓓ 2

Checking Division with Remainders

To check division with remainders, multiply the quotient times the divisor. Then add the remainder.

$$6\overline{)77}\,^{12\ R5}$$

Check:
Multiply: $12 \times 6 = 72$
Add remainder: $72 + 5 = 77$
It checks!

Step-By-Step

In **example 14**, 4 does not divide evenly into 58. The number that is left over is called the remainder. The remainder affects the answer to the problem.

1 Divide 4 into 5 tens.

$$4\overline{)58}\,^{1}$$
$$-4$$

Write 1 in the quotient.

Multiply 4 × 1.

Subtract.

2 Bring down the ones. Then divide 4 into 18. The number left over is the remainder.

$$4\overline{)58}\,^{14}$$
$$-4$$
$$18$$
$$-16$$

Write 4 in the quotient.

Multiply 4 × 4.

Subtract.

3 The quotient tells you how many full cartons Cheyenne needs. The remainder tells you how many extra bottles Cheyenne needs.

She needs _____ full cartons.

She needs _____ extra bottles.

4 How many cartons does Cheyenne need to buy to have enough juice?

She needs to buy _____ cartons.

24 What is 354 ÷ 6?

 Ⓐ 6 R9 Ⓒ 59

 Ⓑ 7 R3 Ⓓ 69

25 Solve.

$$4\overline{)3,404}$$

26 The garden center sold 156 seedlings in packages of 6 seedlings each. How many packages did they sell? Show your work in the space below. Write your answer on the line.

Answer: _____ packages

27 Solve.

$$4\overline{)953}$$

28 What is 909 ÷ 7?

 Ⓐ 119 R6

 Ⓑ 128 R13

 Ⓒ 129 R5

 Ⓓ 129 R6

Go for it!

Test Practice 3: Whole Number Operations

Estimated time: 25 minutes

Directions: Read and answer each question.

1 In the election for class president, Miguel received 178 votes and Maya received 89 votes. By how many votes did Miguel win the election?

Ⓐ 81   Ⓒ 111

Ⓑ 89   Ⓓ 267

2 West High School has two auditoriums. the smaller auditorium seats 556 people. The larger auditorium seats 919 people. How many seats are there in all?

Ⓐ 1,475   Ⓒ 1,243

Ⓑ 1,465   Ⓓ 363

3 Which property of multiplication is shown below?

$$(9 \times 4) \times 5 = 9 \times (4 \times 5)$$

Ⓐ Associative

Ⓑ Commutative

Ⓒ Identity

Ⓓ Zero

4 The snack bar sold 152 mixed-green salads at $3 each. How much did they earn from the sale of those salads?

Ⓐ $155   Ⓒ $456

Ⓑ $304   Ⓓ $3,156

5 Which shows a correct application of the Identity Property of Addition?

Ⓐ $3 + 8 = 8 + 3$

Ⓑ $5 + 0 = 5$

Ⓒ $6 + 2 = 2 + 6$

Ⓓ $7 + (3 + 5) = (7 + 3) + 5$

6 There are 8 fourth-grade classrooms at Washington Elementary School. There are 187 students in fourth grade. Each classroom has about the same number of students. About how many students are in each classroom?

Ⓐ a few more than 20 students

Ⓑ a few less than 20 students

Ⓒ exactly 23 students

Ⓓ exactly 24 students

7 A bus holds 42 people. How many people can 21 buses carry?

Answer: _____

8 George canned 100 pints of tuna. He can store 12 pints in a box. How many boxes does he need to store the canned tuna?

Ⓐ 8

Ⓑ 8 R4

Ⓒ 9

Ⓓ 12

9 Ms. Snow wants to give each of the 29 students in her class 12 stickers. How many stickers does she need?

Ⓐ 87

Ⓑ 248

Ⓒ 348

Ⓓ 870

10 Waukee High School has 3,327 students. Clive High School has 1,688 students. About how many more students go to Waukee than to Clive? Estimate by rounding the numbers to the nearest hundred before finding the difference.

Ⓐ 1,600
Ⓑ 1,700
Ⓒ 4,900
Ⓓ 5,000

11 Mr. Ramos paid $3,079 for a new office computer. He paid $1,853 for a home computer. How much more did he pay for the office computer than for the home computer?

Ⓐ $1,226
Ⓑ $1,826
Ⓒ $4,826
Ⓓ $4,932

12 On Monday 4,325 adults and 2,867 children went to the county fair. How many went to the fair in all?

Ⓐ 2,542
Ⓑ 6,182
Ⓒ 7,192
Ⓓ 7,282

13 What is the quotient?

$$900 \div 30$$

Ⓐ 3,000   Ⓒ 30
Ⓑ 300   Ⓓ 3

14 The 1,564 students at Lincoln School eat lunch during 4 different periods. The same number of students eat during each period. How many students eat each period?

Answer: _____

15 Estimate 65×81. The product is between which numbers?

Ⓐ 450 and 600
Ⓑ 900 and 1,200
Ⓒ 4,800 and 6,300
Ⓓ 9,000 and 12,000

16 Each of the 7 flower beds at Homer Park has an area of 1,220 square feet. What is the total area of the flower beds?

Answer: _____

17 Darrel did this multiplication to check a division problem. He found that he had the right answer.

$$\begin{array}{r} 38 \\ \times\ 7 \\ \hline 266 \end{array}$$

Which could be the division problem?

Ⓐ $38 \div 7$ Ⓒ $266 \div 45$
Ⓑ $45 \div 7$ Ⓓ $266 \div 7$

18 Lewis Stadium has 5,840 seats. There are 8 sections in the stadium. If each section has the same number of seats, how many seats are in each section?

Answer: _____

GO ON ⇨

19 There are 50 straws in a box. Nick bought 20 boxes of straws for his restaurant. How many straws did he buy?

Answer: _____

20 Trayvon bought 3 flats with 48 strawberry plants in each flat. How many rows of 5 plants each can Trayvon plant?

Show OR describe each step of your work, even if you do it in your head ("mental math") or use a calculator. Explain in writing why you chose each of your steps.

Answer: _____

Explanation: _____

_____

_____

_____

_____

STOP

Number Correct/Total = _____/20

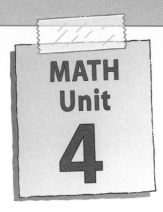

MATH Unit 4

Fractions and Decimals

1 Equivalent Fractions [4.NF.1] [4.NF.5]

2 Fractions and Mixed Numbers [4.NF.3.c]

3 Comparing Fractions [4.NF.2]

4 Adding and Subtracting Fractions [4.NF.3.a] [4.NF.3.b] [4.NF.3.d] [4.NF.5]

5 Adding and Subtracting Mixed Numbers [4.NF.3.c] [4.MD.2]

6 Multiplying a Fraction by a Whole Number [4.NF.4.a] [4.NF.4.b] [4.NF.4.c] [4.MD.2]

7 Fractions and Decimals [4.NF.6]

8 Comparing Decimals [4.NF.7]

Directions: Read and answer each question.

Equivalent Fractions

1 Which fraction is equivalent to $\frac{3}{4}$?

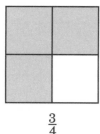

$$\frac{3}{4} \quad = \quad ?$$

Ⓐ $\frac{2}{8}$ Ⓒ $\frac{6}{8}$

Ⓑ $\frac{2}{6}$ Ⓓ $\frac{6}{6}$

Step-By-Step

Follow these steps to solve **example 1**.

1 Look at the first square. Three of the 4 blocks are shaded.

2 Look at the second square. It is the same size as the first square but it is divided into smaller parts. Count the shaded parts. This number will be the *numerator*, the top number in the fraction. Use the number of equal parts in the whole figure as the *denominator*, the bottom number in the fraction.

$$\frac{\text{number of shaded parts}}{\text{total number of equal parts}} = \underline{\qquad}$$

GO ON

Equivalent Fractions

2 Scot wants to add $\frac{3}{10}$ and $\frac{17}{100}$. First, he needs to make the denominators the same. He writes an equivalent fraction for $\frac{3}{10}$ with a denominator of 100. What is it?

Answer: _____

Equivalent Fractions

To find equivalent fractions, multiply or divide the numerator and denominator by the same number.

$$\frac{2}{5} = \frac{2 \times 7}{5 \times 7} = \frac{14}{35} \qquad \frac{12}{18} = \frac{12 \div 6}{18 \div 6} = \frac{2}{3}$$

Fractions and Mixed Numbers

3 Which answer shows $\frac{17}{3}$ as a mixed number?

Ⓐ $\frac{3}{17}$

Ⓑ $5\frac{2}{17}$

Ⓒ $5\frac{2}{5}$

Ⓓ $5\frac{2}{3}$

Changing an Improper Fraction to a Mixed Number

Divide the numerator by the denominator. Write the remainder as the numerator of a fraction. Write the divisor as the denominator.

$$\frac{5}{2} = 5 \div 2 = 2 \text{ R1} = 2\frac{1}{2}$$

Step-By-Step

For **example 2,** look at the denominators of $\frac{3}{10}$ and $\frac{17}{100}$.

1 How many times greater than 10 is [ ] 100?

2 Multiply the numerator and denominator of $\frac{3}{10}$ by 10 to find an equivalent fraction with denominator 100.

$$\frac{3}{10} = \frac{3 \times 10}{10 \times 10} = \frac{}{100}$$

Step-By-Step

The numerator of the fraction in **example 3** is greater than the denominator. The fraction $\frac{17}{3}$ is an *improper fraction*.

1 To change the improper fraction to a mixed number, divide the numerator by the denominator.

$$\begin{array}{r} 5 \\ 3\overline{)17} \\ -15 \\ \hline 2 \end{array}$$

2 Write the remainder as the numerator of a fraction that has the divisor, 3, as the denominator.

$$\frac{17}{3} = 5\frac{}{3}$$

4 Dewan filled some jars with $\frac{1}{4}$ pint of grape jam each. He used $8\frac{3}{4}$ pints of jam. How many jars did he fill with? (Hint: Change $8\frac{3}{4}$ to an improper fraction.)

Ⓐ 28 Ⓒ 35

Ⓑ 34 Ⓓ 83

Changing a Mixed Number to an Improper Fraction

Multiply the whole number times the denominator. Add the numerator. Use the same denominator in the answer.

$$4\frac{2}{3} = \frac{(4 \times 3) + 2}{3} = \frac{14}{3}$$

5 Which symbol makes this number sentence true?

$$\frac{2}{5} \ \square \ \frac{4}{5}$$

Ⓐ $<$ Ⓒ $=$

Ⓑ $>$ Ⓓ $-$

Remember . . .

If two fractions have the same denominator, the one with the greater numerator is greater.

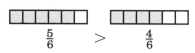

$$\frac{5}{6} \quad > \quad \frac{4}{6}$$

If two fractions have the same numerator, the fraction with the smaller denominator is greater.

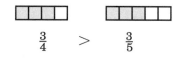

$$\frac{3}{4} \quad > \quad \frac{3}{5}$$

Step-By-Step

In **example 4**, you need to find how many $\frac{1}{4}$ pints there are in $8\frac{3}{4}$ pints. Start by changing $8\frac{3}{4}$ to a fraction.

1 Find the numerator of the mixed number.

$$(8 \times 4) + 3 = \boxed{}$$

2 Use 4 as the denominator and write the fraction.

$$8\frac{3}{4} = \boxed{}$$

3 How many one-fourths are there in 35 fourths?

$$\boxed{}$$

Step-By-Step

Both fractions in **example 5** have a 5 as the denominator. You can compare the fractions by drawing pictures to represent them.

1 Draw five squares. Shade in 2 squares to represent $\frac{2}{5}$.

2 Draw five more squares. Shade in 4 squares to represent $\frac{4}{5}$.

□ □ □ □ □

3 Since the picture showing $\frac{4}{5}$ has the most squares shaded, $\frac{4}{5}$ is greater than $\frac{2}{5}$. Choose the symbol that correctly shows this comparison.

GO ON

Comparing Fractions

6 Which statement correctly compares $\frac{1}{4}$ of a quart and $\frac{5}{8}$ of a quart?

Ⓐ $\frac{1}{4} > \frac{5}{8}$ Ⓒ $\frac{1}{4} < \frac{5}{8}$

Ⓑ $\frac{5}{8} < \frac{1}{4}$ Ⓓ $\frac{5}{8} = \frac{1}{4}$

Another Way

Compare each of the fractions to $\frac{1}{2}$.

$\frac{1}{4}$ is less than $\frac{1}{2}$.

$\frac{5}{8}$ is greater than $\frac{1}{2}$.

So $\frac{1}{4} < \frac{5}{8}$ or $\frac{5}{8} > \frac{1}{4}$.

Step-By-Step

To compare $\frac{1}{4}$ and $\frac{5}{8}$ in **example 6**, first rewrite the fractions so they have a **common denominator**.

1 Look at the denominators. 8 is a multiple of 4. What number multiplied by 4 equals 8?

    Answer:

2 Multiply the numerator and denominator of $\frac{1}{4}$ by 2 to find equivalent fractions.

$$\frac{1}{4} = \frac{1 \times 2}{4 \times 2} = \boxed{}$$

3 The fractions have the same denominator, so compare numerators. Then select the correct answer.

Try It

1 Which fraction is NOT equivalent to $\frac{3}{4}$?

Ⓐ $\frac{9}{12}$

Ⓑ $\frac{12}{15}$

Ⓒ $\frac{15}{20}$

Ⓓ $\frac{75}{100}$

2 Which fraction is the reduced form of $\frac{6}{9}$?

Ⓐ $\frac{1}{3}$

Ⓑ $\frac{12}{18}$

Ⓒ $\frac{3}{3}$

Ⓓ $\frac{2}{3}$

3 What is $\frac{24}{30}$ in simplest form? Show your work in the space provided.

Answer: _____

4 Maria baked 24 cookies. She gave 4 to her neighbor. What fraction of her cookies did she give to her neighbor? Give your answer in simplest form.

Answer: _____

5 Which fraction is NOT equivalent to $\frac{1}{3}$?

Ⓐ $\frac{4}{12}$ Ⓒ $\frac{3}{9}$

Ⓑ $\frac{3}{12}$ Ⓓ $\frac{7}{21}$

6 Which answer shows $\frac{16}{5}$ as a mixed number?

Ⓐ $3\frac{1}{3}$ Ⓒ $2\frac{1}{5}$

Ⓑ $3\frac{1}{5}$ Ⓓ $3\frac{1}{16}$

7 Add the symbol that makes this number sentence true.

$$\frac{2}{7} \;\boxed{}\; \frac{4}{7}$$

Adding and Subtracting Fractions

7 Kevin, Marco, and Darius shared a pizza. Kevin ate $\frac{2}{7}$ of the pizza. Marco ate $\frac{4}{7}$ of the pizza. Darius ate $\frac{1}{7}$ of the pizza.

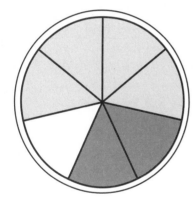

Together, how much pizza did Kevin and Darius eat?

Answer: _____

How much more pizza did Marco eat than Darius?

Answer: _____

Step-By-Step

The fractions in **example 7** have the same denominator. You can add and subtract them by adding and subtracting the numerators.

1 Add to find the total amount of pizza that Kevin and Darius ate.

$$\frac{2}{7} + \frac{1}{7} = \frac{2+1}{7} = \boxed{}$$

2 Subtract to find how much more pizza Marco ate than Darius.

$$\frac{4}{7} - \frac{1}{7} = \frac{4-1}{7} = \boxed{}$$

Adding and Subtracting Fractions

8 Marcus got a sum of $\frac{5}{8}$ when he added some fractions. Which could NOT be the fractions he added?

Ⓐ $\frac{3}{8} + \frac{1}{8} + \frac{1}{8}$

Ⓑ $\frac{1}{8} + \frac{2}{8} + \frac{2}{8}$

Ⓒ $\frac{1}{8} + \frac{1}{8} + \frac{1}{8} + \frac{2}{8}$

Ⓓ $\frac{2}{8} + \frac{2}{8} + \frac{2}{8}$

Adding and Subtracting Fractions

For fractions with the same denominator, add or subtract the numerators. The denominator stays the same.

Adding and Subtracting Mixed Numbers

9 Myra makes her own bird seed mix using $2\frac{3}{8}$ cups of sunflower seeds and $1\frac{3}{8}$ cups of corn. How many cups of bird seed does her recipe make?

Answer: _____ cups

Simplest Form Fractions

A fraction is in simplest form when the numerator and denominator have no common factors except 1.

Step-By-Step

For **example 8**, all of the fractions have 8 as a denominator.

1 Add the numerators to find each sum.

$$\frac{3}{8} + \frac{1}{8} + \frac{1}{8} = \boxed{}$$

$$\frac{1}{8} + \frac{2}{8} + \frac{2}{8} = \boxed{}$$

$$\frac{1}{8} + \frac{1}{8} + \frac{1}{8} + \frac{2}{8} = \boxed{}$$

$$\frac{2}{8} + \frac{2}{8} + \frac{2}{8} = \boxed{}$$

2 Select the answer that does not have a sum of $\frac{5}{8}$.

Step-By-Step

Add the two amounts to find the answer for **example 9**.

1 Add the fractions first. Then add the whole numbers.

$$\begin{array}{r} 2\frac{3}{8} \\ + 1\frac{3}{8} \\ \hline \boxed{} \end{array}$$

2 Decide if the numerator and denominator of $\frac{6}{8}$ have a common factor other than 1.

Factors of 6: 1, 2, 3, 6

Factors of 8: 1, 2, 4, 8

The greatest factor that is common to

both numbers is $\boxed{}$.

3 Divide the numerator and the denominator of the fraction by 2 to write the fraction in simplest form.

$$3\frac{6}{8} = 3\frac{6 \div 2}{8 \div 2} = 3\frac{\boxed{}}{\boxed{}}$$

Adding and Subtracting Mixed Numbers

10 Monty rode his bicycle $7\frac{1}{10}$ kilometers on Monday and $9\frac{7}{10}$ kilometers on Tuesday. How much farther did he ride on Tuesday?

Answer: _____

Step-By-Step

Subtract to find the answer for **example 10**.

1 Subtract the fractions first. Then subtract the whole numbers.

$$9\frac{7}{10}$$
$$-\,7\frac{1}{10}$$

2 Look for common factors in the numerator and denominator of the fraction.

Factors of 6: 1, 2, 3, 6

Factors of 10: 1, 2, 5, 10

The greatest common factor for 6 and 10 is

3 Divide the numerator and the denominator of the fraction by 2 to write the fraction in simplest form.

$$2\frac{6}{10} = 2\frac{6 \div 2}{10 \div 2} = 2\,\underline{}$$

Try It

8 Juan's mom uses $1\frac{2}{3}$ cup of sugar and $1\frac{1}{3}$ cup of brown sugar when she bakes cookies. How much sugar does she use in all?

Answer: _____

9
$$2\frac{1}{4}$$
$$-\,1\frac{1}{4}$$

Answer: _____

10 Which of the following number sentences equals $\frac{7}{8}$?

Ⓐ $\frac{1}{8} + \frac{3}{8} + \frac{3}{8}$

Ⓑ $\frac{2}{8} + \frac{2}{8} + \frac{2}{8}$

Ⓒ $\frac{3}{8} + \frac{1}{8} + \frac{1}{8}$

Ⓓ $\frac{3}{8} + \frac{3}{8} + 1$

GO ON

11 Antonio is making hamburgers. For each, he needs $\frac{1}{4}$ pound of meat. How many pounds of meat does he need to make 7 hamburgers?

Answer: _____ pounds

Think It Through

For **example 11**, one way to model multiplying $\frac{1}{4}$ times 7 is on a number line.

Draw a number line and divide the distance between each whole number into fourths. Count $\frac{1}{4}$ seven times.

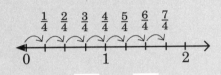

$$7 \times \frac{1}{4} = \frac{\boxed{}}{4} = 1\frac{\boxed{}}{4} \text{ pounds}$$

12 Anna is making costumes for the school play. She needs $\frac{2}{3}$ yard of fabric for each costume. How many yards of fabric does she need for 4 costumes?

Answer: _____ yards

Step-By-Step

One way to find the number of yards of fabric for **example 12** is to make a drawing.

1 Sketch yards of fabric divided into thirds.

2 Cross out four $\frac{2}{3}$ yard pieces.

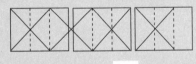

$$4 \times \frac{2}{3} = \frac{8}{3} = 2\frac{\boxed{}}{3} \text{ yards}$$

13 Jamal shaded $\frac{7}{10}$ of this square. Which is the decimal for $\frac{7}{10}$?

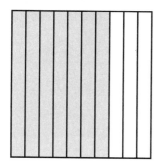

Ⓐ 0.007　　　　　Ⓒ 0.7

Ⓑ 0.07　　　　　Ⓓ 7.0

14 Olivia shaded 0.68 of this square.

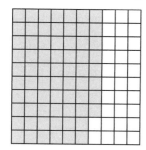

Write a fraction for the part of the square that is shaded.

Answer: _____

Think It Through

You can use a place-value chart to choose the answer for **example 13**.

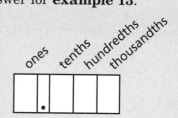

Place each number in the place-value chart. Choose the answer that has 7 in the tenths place.

Think It Through

For **example 14**, *sixty-eight hundredths* of the square is shaded. The place value, hundredths, tells you that the denominator of the fraction is 100. Sixty-eight tells you the numerator.

$$0.68 = \frac{}{100}$$

GO ON

11 How much of the circle is shaded?

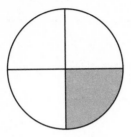

Ⓐ 0.33 Ⓒ $\frac{1}{3}$

Ⓑ $\frac{1}{2}$ Ⓓ 0.25

12 Which decimal or fraction does NOT tell the amount of the rectangle that is shaded?

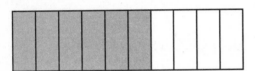

Ⓐ $\frac{3}{5}$ Ⓒ 0.6

Ⓑ 0.35 Ⓓ $\frac{6}{10}$

13 Write eighteen-hundredths as a decimal and as a fraction.

_____ = _____

14 Write two-fifths as a fraction and as a decimal.

_____ = _____

15 Shade 0.5 of this figure.

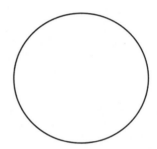

16 $4 \times \frac{2}{3}$

Answer: _____

15 Which symbol correctly compares these two decimals?

$$2.3 \ \square \ 2.18$$

Ⓐ <

Ⓑ >

Ⓒ =

Ⓓ +

Using Place Value to Compare

To compare decimals, line up decimal points.

5.43

5.3

Then compare each place from left to right.

Try It

17 Write the decimals below in order from least to greatest.

1.0   0.1   1.01   0.001

Answer: _____

_____

18 Add the symbol that correctly compares these two decimals.

$$3.30 \ \square \ 3.03$$

Step-By-Step

You can use money to model each decimal in **example 15**.

1 Use 2 dollars and 3 dimes to model 2.3.

2 Use 2 dollars, 1 dime, and 8 pennies to model 2.18.

3 Compare the models. Choose the symbol that correctly compares the two decimals.

Money and Decimals

1
one
A dollar is one.

0.1
one tenth
A dime is one tenth of a dollar.

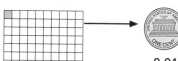

0.01
one hundredth
A penny is one hundredth of a dollar.

Go for it!

Test Practice 4: Fractions and Decimals

Estimated time: 25 minutes

Directions: Read and answer each question.

1 Paul needs $\frac{6}{8}$ cup of milk. Which measure is equivalent to $\frac{6}{8}$ cup?

Ⓐ $\frac{2}{3}$ cup

Ⓑ $\frac{3}{4}$ cup

Ⓒ $1\frac{1}{3}$ cup

Ⓓ $6\frac{1}{8}$ cup

2 Which does NOT describe the shaded part of this grid?

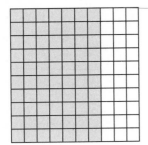

Ⓐ $\frac{7}{10}$

Ⓑ 0.7

Ⓒ $\frac{70}{100}$

Ⓓ 0.07

3 A blueberry pie and an apple pie are each cut into eighths. The blueberry pie has $\frac{3}{8}$ left, and the apple pie has $\frac{4}{8}$ left. Linda put the two pies together into 1 pie pan. How much of the pan was filled?

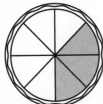
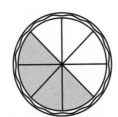

Blueberry pie   Apple pie

Ⓐ $\frac{1}{8}$ Ⓒ $\frac{7}{8}$

Ⓑ $\frac{5}{8}$ Ⓓ $\frac{8}{8}$

4 Which is a true statement?

Ⓐ $0.5 = 5.0$

Ⓑ $0.05 = 0.5$

Ⓒ $0.5 = 0.50$

Ⓓ $0.5 = 0.05$

5 On which number line is the location of point C less than $\frac{3}{8}$?

Ⓐ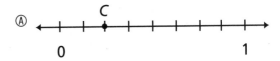

Ⓑ

Ⓒ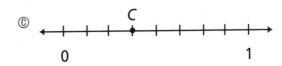

Ⓓ

6 Sandra had $\frac{5}{6}$ of a pizza left. She and her brother ate $\frac{2}{6}$ of the pizza. What fraction of the pizza is left?

Ⓐ $\frac{3}{36}$ Ⓒ $\frac{3}{12}$

Ⓑ $\frac{1}{6}$ Ⓓ $\frac{3}{6}$

7 Which fractions have the same sum as $\frac{2}{10} + \frac{3}{10}$?

Ⓐ $\frac{1}{10} + \frac{3}{10} + \frac{3}{10}$

Ⓑ $\frac{1}{10} + \frac{1}{10} + \frac{3}{10}$

Ⓒ $\frac{2}{10} + \frac{2}{10} + \frac{2}{10}$

Ⓓ $\frac{2}{10} + \frac{1}{10} + \frac{5}{10}$

8 Norm needs $\frac{3}{4}$ cups of milk for each batch of muffins he makes. How many cups of milk does he need for 3 batches of muffins?

Ⓐ $\frac{3}{4}$ c

Ⓑ $\frac{6}{4}$ c

Ⓒ $\frac{9}{4}$ c

Ⓓ $\frac{12}{4}$ c

9 Which equation is illustrated by this model?

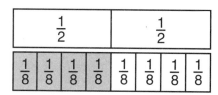

Ⓐ $\frac{4}{8} = \frac{1}{2}$ Ⓒ $\frac{2}{2} + \frac{8}{8} = 1$

Ⓑ $\frac{2}{2} = \frac{4}{8}$ Ⓓ $\frac{1}{2} - \frac{4}{8} = \frac{1}{2}$

10 José picked $\frac{9}{10}$ kilogram of blackberries. Pia picked $\frac{1}{4}$ kilogram of blackberries. Which compares the masses of the blackberries?

Ⓐ $\frac{9}{10} > \frac{1}{4}$

Ⓑ $\frac{1}{4} = \frac{9}{10}$

Ⓒ $\frac{1}{4} > \frac{9}{10}$

Ⓓ $\frac{9}{10} < \frac{1}{4}$

11 Ben rode his bicycle $4\frac{2}{10}$ miles along one trail and $2\frac{3}{10}$ miles along another. How far did he ride in all?

Ⓐ $6\frac{5}{10}$ miles

Ⓑ $6\frac{5}{20}$ miles

Ⓒ $2\frac{1}{10}$ miles

Ⓓ $2\frac{1}{20}$ miles

12 Write the multiplication equation shown on this number line? Then solve it. Write your answer as a mixed number with the fraction in its simplest form.

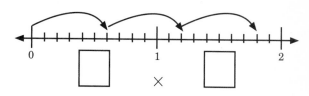

Answer: _____

13 Which improper fraction is equivalent to $3\frac{3}{4}$?

Ⓐ $\frac{15}{4}$

Ⓑ $\frac{15}{3}$

Ⓒ $\frac{33}{4}$

Ⓓ $\frac{34}{3}$

14 Which fraction is equivalent to $\frac{8}{12}$?

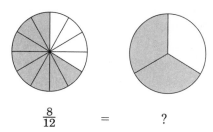

$\frac{8}{12}$ =   ?

Ⓐ $\frac{1}{3}$

Ⓑ $\frac{2}{3}$

Ⓒ $\frac{4}{12}$

Ⓓ $\frac{1}{2}$

15 Which amount of money is less than $62.78?

Ⓐ $67.28

Ⓑ $62.87

Ⓒ $62.08

Ⓓ $68.72

GO ON

16 Christina walked $3\frac{4}{10}$ kilometers in the morning. She walked $1\frac{3}{10}$ kilometers farther in the afternoon. How far did she walk in the afternoon?

Answer: _____

17 Treavor had $3\frac{7}{8}$ cups of berries. He used $1\frac{1}{8}$ cups of berries for some muffins. How many cups of berries were left?

Answer: _____

Show OR describe each step of your work, even if you do it in your head ("mental math") or use a calculator. Explain in writing why you chose each of your steps.

Explanation: _____

_____

_____

_____

_____

_____

_____

18 Which fraction equals 0.13?

Ⓐ $\frac{13}{10}$

Ⓑ $\frac{13}{100}$

Ⓒ $\frac{133}{100}$

Ⓓ $\frac{13}{1000}$

19 Kyle has $3.28. Amber has $3.42. Which symbol correctly compares the amounts of money?

$$\$3.28 \ \square \ \$3.42$$

Ⓐ $<$

Ⓑ $=$

Ⓒ $>$

Ⓓ $+$

20 What mixed number is equal to $\frac{23}{6}$?

Ⓐ $2\frac{3}{6}$

Ⓑ $3\frac{1}{6}$

Ⓒ $3\frac{1}{2}$

Ⓓ $3\frac{5}{6}$

STOP

Points Earned/Total = _____ /20

MATH Unit 5

Measurement and Data

Directions: Read and answer each question.

Converting Measurements

1   Jordan cut 3 feet of copper wire. Which equation shows the number of inches of wire he cut?

Ⓐ $3 \times 12 = 36$

Ⓑ $3 \times 10 = 30$

Ⓒ $3 + 12 = 15$

Ⓓ $36 \div 3 = 12$

Step-By-Step

For **example 1**, you need to know the number of inches in one foot.

1 How many inches are in 1 foot?

[   ] inches

2 Feet × inches per foot = total inches

$3 \times 12 =$ [   ]

Remember . . .

To change from a smaller unit like inches to a larger unit like feet, divide.

smaller to larger → ÷

To change from a larger unit like gallons to a smaller unit like cups, multiply.

larger to smaller → ×

Table of Measures

	U.S. (Customary)	Metric
Length	1 foot = 12 inches 1 yard = 3 feet = 36 inches 1 mile = 5,280 feet	1 centimeter = 10 millimeters 1 meter = 100 centimeters = 1,000 millimeters 1 kilometer = 1,000 meters
Capacity	1 cup = 8 ounces 1 pint = 2 cups 1 quart = 4 cups = 2 pints 1 gallon = 4 quarts	1 liter = 1,000 milliliters
Weight	1 pound = 16 ounces 1 ton = 2,000 pounds	1 kilogram = 1,000 grams

---

Converting Measurements

2 Hank won a trophy that has a mass of 5 kilograms. How many grams is that?

Ⓐ 50 grams   Ⓒ 1,000 grams

Ⓑ 500 grams   Ⓓ 5,000 grams

3 Jillian bought 48 ounces of potatoes. How many pounds of potatoes did she buy?

Ⓐ 1 pound   Ⓒ 3 pounds

Ⓑ 2 pounds   Ⓓ 4 pounds

Another Way

You can make a table to show the relationship between pounds and ounces.

Pounds	Ounces
1	16
2	32
3	48
4	64

Think It Through

For **example 2**, you need to know the number of grams in a kilogram.

$$1 \text{ kilogram (kg)} = 1,000 \text{ grams (g)}$$

Calculate how many grams are in 5 kilograms.

To convert a larger unit to a smaller unit, multiply.

$$5 \text{ kg} \times 1,000 \text{ g/kg} = \boxed{} \text{ g}$$

Step-By-Step

For **example 3**, you need to know the number of ounces in a pound.

$$1 \text{ pound (lb)} = 16 \text{ ounces (oz)}$$

1 You need to find out how many pounds are equal to 48 ounces.

2 To convert a smaller unit to a larger unit, divide.

$$48 \text{ oz} \div 16 \text{ oz/lb} = \boxed{} \text{ lb}$$

1 Trevor made 2 gallons of punch. How many quarts of punch did he make?

Answer: _____

2 Ms. Ruiz bought 32 ounces of sliced turkey and 16 ounces of sliced roast beef. How many pounds of sliced meat did she buy in all?

Ⓐ 1 pound   Ⓒ 3 pounds

Ⓑ 2 pounds   Ⓓ 4 pounds

3 Which measurement is equal to 100 millimeters?

Ⓐ 10 centimeters

Ⓑ 100 centimeters

Ⓒ 1 meter

Ⓓ 10 meters

4 Which measurement is equal to 2 kilograms?

Ⓐ 20 grams

Ⓑ 200 grams

Ⓒ 2,000 grams

Ⓓ 20,000 grams

5 How many inches are there in 3 yards?

Ⓐ 12 inches   Ⓒ 72 inches

Ⓑ 36 inches   Ⓓ 108 inches

6 How can you change 2 meters to centimeters?

Ⓐ Multiply by 10.

Ⓑ Multiply by 100.

Ⓒ Divide by 10.

Ⓓ Divide by 100.

7 Wu bought 4 kilograms of pineapples. How many grams did he buy?

Answer: _____

8 Mr. Garcia drinks 3 quarts of water each day. How many cups of water is that?

Ⓐ 12 cups   Ⓒ 8 cups

Ⓑ 10 cups   Ⓓ 4 cups

GO ON

Some tests include questions in which you must write an explanation of how you solved the problem. You may also be asked to show your work, draw graphs, or make diagrams. The example below will give you practice answering such questions.

Time and Distance

4 A train leaves at 5:15. It travels 40 miles per hour for $1\frac{1}{2}$ hours.

When does it arrive? How many miles is the trip?

Show OR describe each step of your work, even if you did it in your head ("mental math") or used a calculator. Explain in writing why you chose each of your steps.

Answer: _____

Explanation: _____

_____

_____

_____

_____

_____

Time

1 minute = 60 seconds

1 hour = 60 minutes

1 day = 24 hours

Step-By-Step

Decide how you can use the information given in **example 4** to find the arrival time and the number of miles the train travels.

My Plan: *I will use a clock face to figure out what time it is $1\frac{1}{2}$ hours after 5:15. To find distance, I will multiply the number of hours the train traveled by the number of miles per hour it traveled.*

Step 1: I can multiply $60 \times \frac{1}{2} = 30$ to find there are 30 minutes in $\frac{1}{2}$ hour. To find the time 1 hour and 30 minutes after 5:15. I will start at 5:15.

If I add 30 minutes to 5:15, the time is 5:45. One hour after 5:45 is 6:45.

The train arrives at 6:45.

Step 2: The train traveled at 40 miles per hour. It traveled for $1\frac{1}{2}$ hours. So to find distance, I will multiply 40 times $1\frac{1}{2}$. First I have to change $1\frac{1}{2}$ to a fraction.

$$40 \times 1\frac{1}{2} = 40 \times \frac{3}{2} = \frac{120}{2} = 60$$

The train traveled 60 miles.

Explanation: *I counted forward $1\frac{1}{2}$ hours from 5:15 to find the time the train arrived. I multiplied 40 miles per hour times $1\frac{1}{2}$ hours to find the distance the train traveled.*

9 Brian's train left North End Station at 8:48 a.m. It arrived at South End Station at 9:55 a.m. How long was the trip?

Answer: _____

10 Soccer practice started at 3:10 p.m. It lasted 1 hour and 25 minutes. What time was soccer practice over?

Answer: _____

11 Wanda has a dentist appointment at 2:00 p.m. It takes her 1 hour and 10 minutes to get to the dentist's office. What time should she leave home?

Ⓐ 3:10 p.m.   Ⓒ 1:50 p.m.
Ⓑ 2:50 p.m.   Ⓓ 12:50 p.m.

12 A movie starts at 7:05 p.m. It is 1 hour and 40 minutes long. What time does the movie end?

Ⓐ 5:25 p.m.   Ⓒ 8:25 p.m.
Ⓑ 7:45 p.m.   Ⓓ 8:45 p.m.

Line Plots

5 A group of friends weighed their shoes. These are the weights in pounds:

$1, \frac{7}{8}, \frac{7}{8}, \frac{1}{2}, \frac{3}{4}, \frac{3}{8}, 1\frac{1}{8}, \frac{3}{4}, \frac{7}{8}, 1\frac{1}{4}$

They want to make a line plot to show the data. Which line should they use?

Ⓐ
$0 \quad \frac{1}{2} \quad 1 \quad 1\frac{1}{2} \quad 2 \quad 2\frac{1}{2} \quad 3 \quad 3\frac{1}{2} \quad 4$

Ⓑ
$\frac{1}{4} \quad \frac{3}{8} \quad \frac{1}{2} \quad \frac{5}{8} \quad \frac{3}{4} \quad \frac{7}{8} \quad 1 \quad 1\frac{1}{8} \quad 1\frac{1}{4}$

Ⓒ
$0 \quad \frac{1}{4} \quad \frac{1}{2} \quad \frac{3}{4} \quad 1 \quad 1\frac{1}{4} \quad 1\frac{1}{2} \quad 1\frac{3}{4} \quad 2$

Ⓓ
$\frac{5}{8} \quad \frac{3}{4} \quad \frac{7}{8} \quad 1 \quad 1\frac{1}{8} \quad 1\frac{1}{4} \quad 1\frac{3}{8} \quad 1\frac{1}{2}$

Step-By-Step

For **example 5**, choose a scale that includes all of the weights and not too many greater or lesser weights.

1 What is the weight of the lightest shoes?

2 What is the weight of the heaviest shoes?

3 Which scale includes all of the weights?

GO ON

Line Plots

6 Carolyn measured 15 crickets and made this line plot of their lengths.

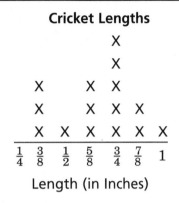

What is the difference between the lengths of the longest and shortest crickets?

Answer: _____

Perimeter of a Rectangle

7 Gretchen is putting a fence around the perimeter of her garden. The garden is a 7-foot by 12-foot rectangle.

How many feet of fence does she need?

Answer: _____ feet

Perimeter of a Rectangle

8 A square frame has a perimeter of 44 inches. How long is each side of the square?

Answer:_____ inches

Think It Through

For **example 8**, remember that a square has 4 same-length sides, so the perimeter is 4 times a side length, $P = 4s$. For this square, $P = 44$. Divide to find s.

$$44 = 4s$$
$$44 \div 4 = s$$
$$\boxed{} = s$$

Area of a Rectangle

9 What is the area of this rectangle?

4 in.

8 in.

Ⓐ 12 in.²   Ⓒ 24 in.²
Ⓑ 32 in.²   Ⓓ 4 in.²

Step-By-Step

Use these two methods to find the area of a rectangle, as in **example 9**.

1 You can divide the rectangle into square units and count them. Here is the 8 by 4 rectangle divided into square units. How many units are there?

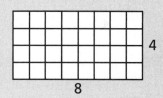

4

8

2 An easier and faster way to find the area of a rectangle is to multiply the length times the width.

$$l \times w = A$$
$$8 \times 4 = \boxed{} \text{ in.}^2$$

Remember . . .

Area is always written in square units.

square inches   or   *sq in.*   or   *in.*²

GO ON

Area of a Rectangle

10 Sophia's bedroom is a rectangle. It has an area of 120 square feet. It is 10 feet wide. What is the length of Sophia's bedroom?

Answer: _____ feet

Step-By-Step®

Use the area formula to find the length of the bedroom for **example 10**.

1 Substitute the numbers you know into the formula $l \times w = A$.

$$l \times \boxed{} = \boxed{}$$

2 Rewrite the multiplication as a division.

$$l \times 10 = 120$$

$$l = 120 \div \boxed{}$$

3 Solve for l.

$$l = 120 \div 10 = \boxed{}$$

Try It

13 Find the area of a square with a side of 12 cm.

Answer: _____

14 Rob has a garden that is 20 feet wide and 10 feet long. What is the area of the garden?

Ⓐ 60 ft²   Ⓒ 200 ft²

Ⓑ 10 ft   Ⓓ 30 ft

15 What is the area of the figure below?

2 yd
5 yd

Ⓐ 10 yd²   Ⓒ 14 yd²

Ⓑ 7 yd²   Ⓓ 3 yd

Figure the perimeters and areas of these two rectangles. Then fill in the blanks and circle the choices in the statements below.

4 in.   Figure C   5 in.

Figure D   3 in.   6 in.

16 Perimeter of Figure C = _____.

Area of Figure C = _____.

17 Perimeter of Figure D = _____.

Area of Figure D = _____.

18 The perimeters of the two rectangles are (the same   different).

19 The areas of the two rectangles are (the same   different).

11 What is the measure of ∠A?

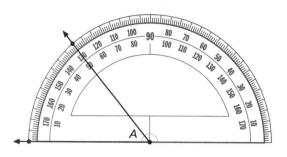

ⓐ 35° ⓒ 80°

ⓑ 50° ⓓ 130°

Think It Through

The angle in **example 11** is measured using a **protractor**. A protractor is marked in degrees. A protractor has two scales so you can read angles that open from the left or from the right.

One side of the angle is lined up with the zero degree mark on one of the protractor scales. Read the angle's measure where the other side crosses the **same scale**.

What is the measure of the angle? _____°

Degrees

A **degree** is $\frac{1}{360}$ of a circle. The symbol for degree is °.

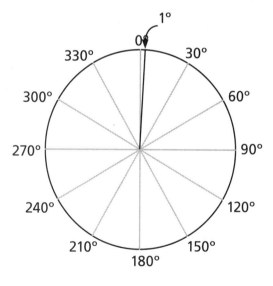

Measurement and Data **81**

Finding Angle Measures

12 Angle *CAB* measures 40°. Angle *DAB* measures 122°.

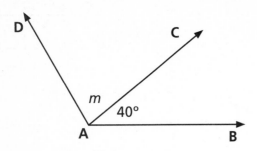

What is the measure of angle *DAC*?

Answer: _____

Step-By-Step

For **example 12**, The measure of angle *CAB* plus the measure of angle *DAC* equals the measure of angle *DAB*.

1 Write an equation. The measure of ∠*CAB* is 40°. The measure of ∠*DAC* is *m*. The measure of ∠*DAB* is 122°.

$$40° + m = 122°$$

2 Rewrite the addition as a subtraction.

$$m = 122° - \boxed{}$$

3 Find the measure of angle *DAC*.

$$m = 122° - 40° = \boxed{}$$

Naming Angles

Name an angle by naming a point on each of its sides with the vertex in the middle. The symbol for angle is ∠. This is ∠*CAB* or ∠*BAC*.

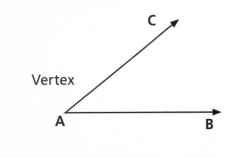

13 What is the measure of ∠*PQS*?

Answer: _____

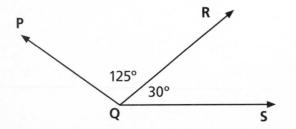

Think It Through

For **example 13**, the measure of angle *PQS* is the sum of the measures of angles *PQR* and *RQS*. The measure of angle *PQR* is 125°. The measure of angle *RQS* is 30°.

$$m = 125° + 30°$$

$$m = \boxed{}$$

Go for it!

Test Practice 5: Measurement and Data

Estimated time: 20 minutes

Directions: Read and answer each question.

1 Hanna takes her dog on a walk around the block. The block is 88 yards long and 60 yards wide. How far does she walk?

Ⓐ 306 yards   Ⓒ 176 yards

Ⓑ 296 yards   Ⓓ 148 yards

2 Which measurement is equal to 2 kilograms?

Ⓐ 20 grams

Ⓑ 200 grams

Ⓒ 2,000 grams

Ⓓ 20,000 grams

3 The area of this deck is 96 square meters. What is the measure of side *s*?

8 meters

s

Answer: _____

4 Which statement is true?

Ⓐ A rotation of 360° is a full turn.

Ⓑ A half turn is 90°.

Ⓒ You can draw a circle by drawing a 180° turn.

Ⓓ A 270° turn makes a half circle.

5 The line plot shows the amount of time Pia spent practicing her drum for 10 days.

Time Spent Practicing
X X
X X   X
X X X X X
$\frac{1}{2}$ 1 $1\frac{1}{2}$ 2 $2\frac{1}{2}$
Time (in Hours)

How long did she spend practicing over those 10 days?

Answer: _____

6 Which statement is true?

Ⓐ 4 yards is more than 15 feet.

Ⓑ 52 inches is less than 2 yards.

Ⓒ 4 meters is more than 5,000 centimeters.

Ⓓ 10 kilometers is less than 4,000 meters.

7 David used 40 feet of braid to trim the edges of a quilt that is 12 feet long. How wide is the quilt? Use the formula $P = 2(l + w)$.

Ⓐ $3\frac{1}{3}$ ft   Ⓒ 14 ft

Ⓑ 8 ft   Ⓓ 28 ft

GO ON ⇨

8 How can you change 2 meters to centimeters?

Ⓐ Multiply by 10.

Ⓑ Multiply by 100.

Ⓒ Divide by 10.

Ⓓ Divide by 100.

9 What is the measure of this angle?

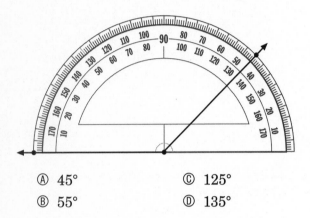

Ⓐ 45°   Ⓒ 125°

Ⓑ 55°   Ⓓ 135°

10 What is the measure of angle *ADB*?

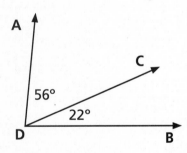

Ⓐ 34°

Ⓑ 68°

Ⓒ 78°

Ⓓ 102°

11 Alden's baseball practice lasted $1\frac{1}{2}$ hours. How many minutes is that?

Answer: _____

12 Maggie made this line plot showing the weights of some pieces of cheese in her shop.

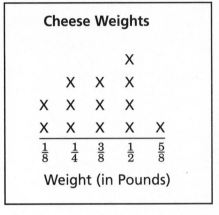

What is the difference between the weight of the heaviest and the lightest pieces of cheese?

Answer: _____

13 Which rectangle has an area of 24 cm² and a perimeter of 20 cm?

Ⓐ
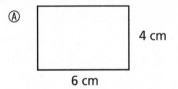

Ⓑ
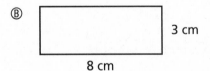

Ⓒ

Ⓓ
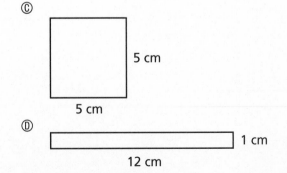

14 Angle *PQR* measures 150°. What is the measure of angle *SQR*?

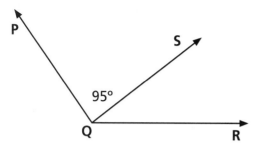

Ⓐ 245°

Ⓑ 125°

Ⓒ 95°

Ⓓ 55°

15 A square has a perimeter of 40 inches. How long is each side of the square?

Ⓐ 20 in.   Ⓒ 10 in.

Ⓑ 14 in.   Ⓓ 8 in.

16 Janelle wants to tile this wall with 1×1 ft. tiles.

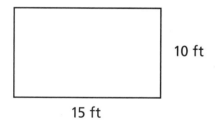

10 ft

15 ft

How can she figure out how much tile she needs?

Ⓐ Multiply 10 times 15.

Ⓑ Add 10 and 15.

Ⓒ Add 10 and 15 and then multiply by 2.

Ⓓ Multiply 10 times 15 and then multiply by 2.

17 Use the protractor to sketch a 65° angle.

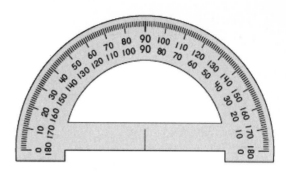

Show OR describe each step of your work. Explain in writing why you chose each of your steps.

Explanation: _____

_____

_____

_____

_____

_____

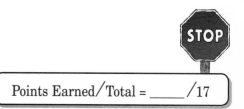

Points Earned / Total = _____ / 17

MATH Unit 6

Geometry

Directions: Read and answer each question.

Elements of Geometry

1   Which figure is made up of 3 line segments and 3 endpoints?

Geometric Elements

A **point** is an exact position.   •

A **line** is a set of points that goes on and on in both directions.   ←→

A **line segment** is a part of a line. It has 2 endpoints.   •—•

A **ray** has 1 endpoint and one end that goes on and on.   •→

An **angle** is made up of 2 rays that have the same endpoint.

Step-By-Step

To solve **example 1**, you must identify line segments and points.

1   A **line segment** is a part of a line with two endpoints (•—•). Which figures have 3 line segments?

figures ☐ and ☐

2   A **point** is an exact position (•). Which figures have exactly 3 points?

figures ☐ and ☐

3   Which figure has both 3 line segments and 3 endpoints?

figure ☐

Elements of Geometry

2 Bill drew a point. Then he used a ruler to draw 2 rays from the point. Which figure did he draw?

ⓐ a square

ⓑ a triangle

ⓒ an angle

ⓓ an arrow

Step-By-Step

To see what figure Bill drew in **example 2**, follow his steps.

1 Draw a point.

2 Use a ruler. Draw a ray from the point.

3 Draw another ray from the same point. Then identify the figure you drew.

Classifying Angles

3 Classify this angle.

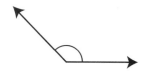

ⓐ right

ⓑ acute

ⓒ obtuse

ⓓ straight

Step-By-Step

In **example 3**, compare the angle to a 90° angle. The corner of a piece of paper is a 90° angle.

1 Ask yourself: Is the angle the same as the corner of a piece of paper?

No, it is larger than the corner of a piece of paper.

2 An angle that is larger than the corner of a piece of paper is more than 90°. Study the *Classifying Angles* box on the next page. What is the name of an angle that is more than 90°?

Classifying Angles

4 Audrey drew a 70° angle. What type of angle did she draw?

Answer: _____

Classifying Angles

Two rays that have the same endpoint form an **angle**. The endpoint is called the **vertex**. Angles are classified by their size.

A **right angle** is exactly 90°, like a square corner.

An **obtuse angle** is greater than 90° but less than 180°.

An **acute angle** is less than 90°.

A **straight angle** is a straight line, exactly 180°.

1 What kind of turn is a 180° angle?

Answer: _____

2 Draw an example of an acute angle in the space below.

3 Write the name of the angle shown below.

Answer: _____

4 Which statement is NOT true?

Ⓐ A $\frac{3}{4}$ turn corresponds with a 270° angle.

Ⓑ A right angle is exactly 90°.

Ⓒ A 360° angle makes a half turn.

Ⓓ Two 90° angles make a straight line.

5 Which of the angles is an obtuse angle?

Ⓐ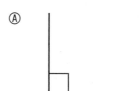

Ⓑ

Ⓒ

Ⓓ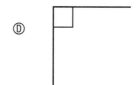

GO ON

5   Which describes this triangle?

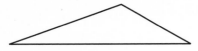

   Ⓐ   acute triangle

   Ⓑ   obtuse triangle

   Ⓒ   right triangle

   Ⓓ   straight triangle

Think It Through

Classify the triangle in **example 5** by its angles. It has two acute angles and one obtuse angle.

Study the *Classifying Triangles* box below. What type of triangle is this?

Classifying Triangles

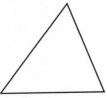

Acute Triangle
All angles are less than 90°.

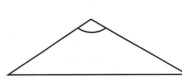

Obtuse Triangle
One angle is greater than 90°.

Right Triangle
One angle measures 90°.

6   A triangle has three acute angles. Classify the triangle.

   Ⓐ   acute triangle

   Ⓑ   obtuse triangle

   Ⓒ   right triangle

   Ⓓ   straight triangle

Think It Through

When answering **example 6**, remember that an acute angle is an angle that is less than 90°. Which type of triangle has three angles that are less than 90°?

6 Name the triangle.

Answer: _____

7 Draw a right triangle in the space below.

8 Label the triangles as right, obtuse, or acute.

_____

_____

_____

9 Which of the triangles below is a right triangle?

Ⓐ

Ⓑ

Ⓒ

Ⓓ

GO ON

7 Which best describes this pair of line segments?

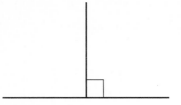

Ⓐ parallel

Ⓑ intersecting but not perpendicular

Ⓒ perpendicular

Ⓓ neither parallel nor intersecting

Think It Through

For **example 7**, look at the line segments. Then ask yourself these questions.

• Do the line segments meet or cross?

• Do the line segments meet at a right angle?

Use the *Pairs of Lines* box below to help answer the question.

Remember . . .

A **right angle** is an angle with a square corner.

The symbol ⌐ shows a right angle.

Pairs of Lines

A pair of lines can be described in these three ways.

Parallel	**Perpendicular**	**Intersecting but not Perpendicular**
These lines never meet. They are always the same distance apart.	The angles where these lines meet are right angles.	The angles where these lines meet are not right angles.
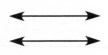		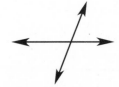

8 Which of these quadrilaterals has opposite sides that are equal length and four right angles?

Ⓐ rhombus

Ⓑ parallelogram

Ⓒ trapezoid

Ⓓ square

Step-By-Step

Review the *Quadrilaterals* box below to answer **example 8**.

1 Find the answer choices that have opposite sides that are equal length.

2 Find the answer choices that have four right angles.

3 Which answer choice has both four right angles and opposite sides that are equal length?

9 Which statement correctly compares a rhombus and a parallelogram?

Ⓐ Both have opposite sides parallel.

Ⓑ Both have all sides equal.

Ⓒ Both have all angles equal.

Ⓓ Both have right angles.

Think It Through

To answer **example 9**, compare each statement to the descriptions of a rhombus and a parallelogram in the *Quadrilaterals* box.

Which statement is true of BOTH quadrilaterals?

Quadrilaterals

Square

- Has four right angles
- All sides are equal
- Opposite sides are parallel

Rhombus

- Opposite angles are equal
- All sides are equal
- Opposite sides are parallel

Trapezoid

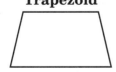

- Has one pair of opposite parallel sides

Rectangle

- Has four right angles
- Opposite sides are equal
- Opposite sides are parallel

Parallelogram

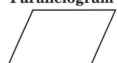

- Opposite angles are equal
- Opposite sides are equal
- Opposite sides are parallel

 GO ON

Some tests include questions in which you must write an explanation of how you solved the problem. You may also be asked to show your work, draw graphs, or make diagrams. The example below will give you practice answering such questions.

Comparing Geometric Figures

10 Compare a rhombus and a rectangle. Describe how they are alike and how you can tell them apart.

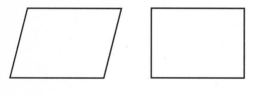

Rhombus   Rectangle

Explanation: _____

_____

_____

_____

_____

_____

_____

_____

_____

Step-By-Step

Plan how you will compare the quadrilaterals for **example 10**. Then show your work and explain your thinking. Write clearly and label each step as in the example below.

My plan: *I will think about the sides and angles of the quadrilaterals and tell how they are alike and how they are different.*

Step 1: Describe the sides and angles of a rhombus. A rhombus has:

   4 equal length sides

   opposite sides parallel

   opposite sides equal

   opposite angles equal

Step 2: Describe the sides and angles of a rectangle. A rectangle has:

   2 pairs of equal length sides

   opposite sides parallel

   opposite sides equal

   opposite angles equal

   4 right angles

Step 3: Tell how the two quadrilaterals are alike. Both have:

   opposite sides parallel

   opposite sides equal

   opposite angles equal

Step 4: Tell how they are different.

   A rectangle has 4 right angles, but a rhombus does not.

   A rhombus has 4 equal sides, but a rectangle does not.

10 Which diagram shows parallel lines?

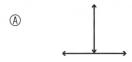

Ⓐ

Ⓑ

Ⓒ

Ⓓ

11 Which statement is NOT true?

Ⓐ Perpendicular lines intersect at right angles.

Ⓑ Parallel lines never intersect.

Ⓒ All lines cross at some point.

Ⓓ Parallel lines stay the same distance apart.

12 Draw an example of perpendicular lines.

13 Draw a rhombus in the space below.

14 Which statement is NOT true?

Ⓐ All squares are rectangles.

Ⓑ All trapezoids are quadrilaterals.

Ⓒ All rhombuses are parallelograms.

Ⓓ A rectangle has acute angles.

15 Name the figure below.

Answer: _____

16 Name the figure below.

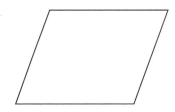

Answer: _____

GO ON

11 Which figure has exactly one line of symmetry?

Ⓐ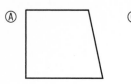

Ⓒ

Ⓑ

Ⓓ

Testing for Symmetry

If the shapes on each side of a fold line match exactly, the fold line is a **line of symmetry.**

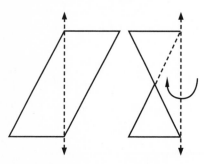

A line of symmetry

Not a line of symmetry

Step-By-Step

Think of folding each figure in **example 11** so that the two halves match exactly. The fold line is a line of symmetry.

1 Draw as many lines of symmetry as you can for each figure.

No line of symmetry

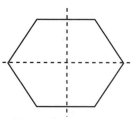

2 lines of symmetry

1 line of symmetry

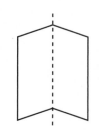

2 lines of symmetry

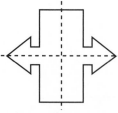

2 Choose the figure that has just one line of symmetry.

17 Draw two lines of symmetry on the figure below.

18 Which shape does NOT show a line of symmetry?

Ⓐ

Ⓑ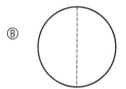

Ⓒ

Ⓓ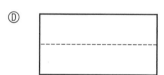

19 Draw one line of symmetry on the figure below.

20 Which figure is an example of symmetry?

Figure A

Figure B

Answer: _____

GO ON

Test Practice 6: Geometry

Estimated time: 20 minutes

Directions: Read and answer each question.

1 Which angle is a right angle?

Ⓐ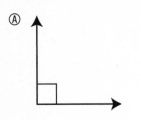

Ⓑ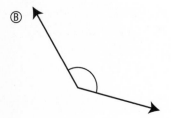

Ⓒ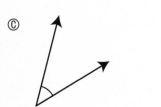

Ⓓ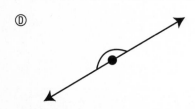

2 On which clock are the hands perpendicular?

Ⓐ   Ⓒ

Ⓑ  Ⓓ

3 Classify this angle.

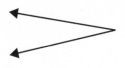

Ⓐ acute
Ⓑ right
Ⓒ obtuse
Ⓓ straight

4 In which pair are the shoes parallel?

Ⓐ

Ⓑ

Ⓒ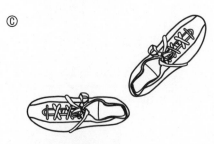

Ⓓ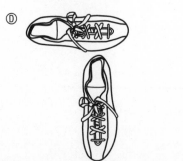

5 Which statement is NOT true?

Ⓐ A right angle is an angle with a square corner

Ⓑ Parallel lines never intersect.

Ⓒ All shapes have lines of symmetry.

Ⓓ Lines can intersect but not be perpendicular.

6 Which answer shows a line of symmetry?

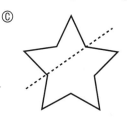
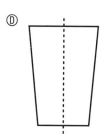

7 Which is made of 2 rays with the same endpoint?

Ⓐ angle

Ⓑ line segment

Ⓒ polygon

Ⓓ triangle

8 An angle has a measure greater than 90° and less than 180°. What type of angle is it?

Answer: _____

9 Which statement is NOT a correct comparison of the rectangle and the square shown?

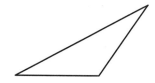

Ⓐ Both have opposite sides parallel.

Ⓑ Both have four sides the same length.

Ⓒ Both have opposite angles equal.

Ⓓ Both have four right angles.

10 Classify this triangle.

Ⓐ acute

Ⓑ right

Ⓒ obtuse

Ⓓ straight

11 Which letter has two lines of symmetry?

Ⓐ **B** Ⓒ **L**

Ⓑ **S** Ⓓ **X**

12 Which figure has 2 endpoints?

GO ON

13 Which quadrilateral has exactly one pair of parallel sides and two obtuse angles?

Ⓐ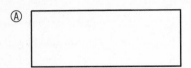

Ⓑ

Ⓒ

Ⓓ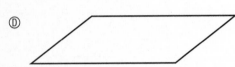

14 How many lines of symmetry does this figure have?

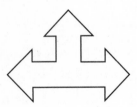

Ⓐ zero

Ⓑ one

Ⓒ two

Ⓓ more than two

15 Which figure has perpendicular sides?

Ⓐ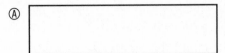

Ⓑ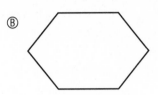

Ⓒ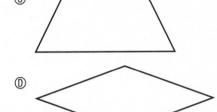

Ⓓ

16 All three angles of a triangle are the same measure. Classify the triangle by its angles.

Answer: _____

Points Earned/Total = _____ /16

Mastery Test

Estimated time: 45 minutes

Directions: Read each question and choose the best answer.

1   What is the value of 6 in 6,849,321?

Ⓐ *six hundred*

Ⓑ *six thousand*

Ⓒ *six hundred-thousand*

Ⓓ *six million*

2   What is the rule for this pattern?

1, 4, 16, 64, 256, . . .

Ⓐ Multiply by 4.

Ⓑ Multiply by 2.

Ⓒ Add 2.

Ⓓ Add 4.

3   What does x equal in this equation?

$5 + x = 13$

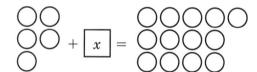

Ⓐ $x = 6$

Ⓑ $x = 8$

Ⓒ $x = 18$

Ⓓ $x = 21$

4   The population of Marysville is 540,712. Which answer shows 540,712 in word form?

Ⓐ *five hundred forty thousand, seven hundred twelve*

Ⓑ *fifty-four thousand, seven hundred twenty-one*

Ⓒ *fifty-four thousand, seven hundred twelve*

Ⓓ *five hundred forty and seven hundred twelve*

5   Antonio picked 24 cups of blackberries. That is 8 times as many cups as Donna picked. Which equation can be used to find the number of cups of blackberries Donna picked?

Ⓐ $24 \times 8 = b$

Ⓑ $b + 8 = 24$

Ⓒ $8 \div b = 24$

Ⓓ $24 = 8 \times b$

6   Wendy practices her violin $\frac{1}{2}$ hour each day. How many hours does she practice in a week (7 days)?

Ⓐ $\frac{1}{14}$ hours

Ⓑ $\frac{2}{7}$ hours

Ⓒ $\frac{7}{14}$ hours

Ⓓ $\frac{7}{2}$ hours

7   Which answer shows a factor pair for 56?

Ⓐ 3×18

Ⓑ 4×14

Ⓒ 6×7

Ⓓ 8×8

8   Yukie's address is a prime number. Which could be her address?

Ⓐ 17 Elm Street

Ⓑ 26 Elm Street

Ⓒ 39 Elm Street

Ⓓ 45 Elm Street

GO ON

9 Which shows the same type of pattern as the one below?

Ⓐ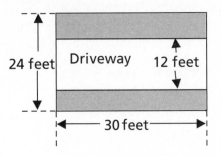

13 Vicky wants to plant grass on each side of her driveway.

24 feet | Driveway | 12 feet
30 feet

Which box of grass seed should she buy?

Ⓐ Covers 250 square feet

Ⓑ Covers 400 square feet

Ⓒ Covers 600 square feet

Ⓓ Covers 800 square feet

10 Steve's height is a multiple of 8. Which could be Steve's height?

Ⓐ 52 inches
Ⓑ 66 inches
Ⓒ 72 inches
Ⓓ 81 inches

11 Which comparison is NOT true?

Ⓐ $346,019 > 346,372$
Ⓑ $679,511 > 671,064$
Ⓒ $129,002 < 129,008$
Ⓓ $762,426 < 762,822$

12 Jason built two birdhouses. One is $11\frac{3}{8}$ inches tall. The other is $14\frac{5}{8}$ inches tall. How much taller is the second birdhouse than the first?

Ⓐ $2\frac{2}{8}$ inches
Ⓑ $3\frac{2}{8}$ inches
Ⓒ $3\frac{4}{8}$ inches
Ⓓ 26 inches

14 Which number rounded to the nearest thousand is NOT 35,000?

Ⓐ 34,680   Ⓒ 35,050
Ⓑ 35,200   Ⓓ 33,900

15 Two pilots have flown 56,319 and 74,112 total miles. To the nearest thousand, how many more miles has the second pilot flown than the first pilot?

Ⓐ 10,000   Ⓒ 20,000
Ⓑ 18,000   Ⓓ 22,000

16 Jim bought 6 boxes of oranges. There are 48 oranges in each box. He uses 10 oranges for each glass of orange juice. How many full glasses, *g*, of orange juice can he make?

Ⓐ *g* = 27   Ⓒ *g* = 29

Ⓑ *g* = 28   Ⓓ *g* = 30

17 During one month, Mostly Music sold 16,708 CDs. The next month they sold 20,416 CDs. How many more CDs did they sell the second month?

Ⓐ 3,708   Ⓒ 4,718

Ⓑ 3,718   Ⓓ 16,312

18 Amy drew a line and a line segment. Which is her drawing?

Ⓐ    Ⓒ

Ⓑ 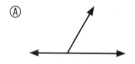   Ⓓ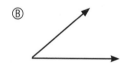

19 For which product is 3,600 a reasonable estimate?

Ⓐ 12 × 29

Ⓑ 42 × 86

Ⓒ 72 × 15

Ⓓ 96 × 53

20 Seferina knitted $\frac{3}{9}$ of a scarf on Monday and $\frac{2}{9}$ of the scarf on Tuesday. What fraction of the scarf did she knit in those two days?

Ⓐ $\frac{5}{9}$ Ⓒ $\frac{6}{81}$

Ⓑ $\frac{5}{18}$ Ⓓ $\frac{1}{9}$

21 Which pair of fractions has a sum of $\frac{3}{8}$?

Ⓐ $\frac{1}{8} + \frac{2}{8}$

Ⓑ $\frac{1}{8} + \frac{4}{8}$

Ⓒ $\frac{2}{8} + \frac{2}{8}$

Ⓓ $\frac{2}{8} + \frac{3}{8}$

22 Jason wrote the equation $56 = 8 \times n$. Which problem could he have been solving?

Ⓐ I rode my bike 56 kilometers. That is 8 times farther than I rode last week. How far did I ride last week?

Ⓑ I rode my bike 8 kilometers. I am riding 56 kilometers in all. How much farther do I have to ride?

Ⓒ I rode my bike 56 kilometers. That is 8 kilometers farther than I rode last week. How far did I ride last week?

Ⓓ I rode my bike 8 kilometers. I have 56 kilometers farther to ride. How far will I ride in all?

23 Phil colored $\frac{9}{12}$ of these squares.

What fraction is equivalent to $\frac{9}{12}$?

Ⓐ $\frac{3}{4}$ Ⓒ $\frac{3}{7}$

Ⓑ $\frac{2}{3}$ Ⓓ $\frac{1}{19}$

GO ON

24 Which statement is true?

Ⓐ $\frac{5}{7} < \frac{1}{2}$

Ⓑ $\frac{3}{8} > \frac{3}{4}$

Ⓒ $\frac{2}{3} < \frac{5}{6}$

Ⓓ $\frac{3}{8} = \frac{8}{10}$

25 Luis cut $\frac{4}{10}$ meters of rope. What is the decimal for the amount of rope he cut?

Ⓐ 0.004 meters

Ⓑ 0.04 meters

Ⓒ 0.4 meters

Ⓓ 4 meters

26 Which fraction is equal to $6\frac{2}{3}$?

Ⓐ $\frac{18}{3}$

Ⓑ $\frac{20}{3}$

Ⓒ $\frac{26}{3}$

Ⓓ $\frac{62}{3}$

27 Which statement is equal to $7 \times (3 \times 2)$?

Ⓐ $7 + 6$

Ⓑ $(7 \times 3) \times 2$

Ⓒ $7 + (3 + 2)$

Ⓓ $(7 + 3) \times (7 + 2)$

28 Mora bought 4 kilograms of fancy cat food. How many grams did she buy?

Ⓐ 4,000 grams

Ⓑ 400 grams

Ⓒ 40 grams

Ⓓ $\frac{1}{4}$ gram

29 A square has the same perimeter as this rectangle.

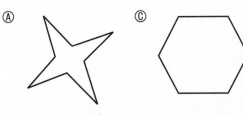

12 m

18 m

What is the length of each side of the square?

Ⓐ 12 m

Ⓑ 15 m

Ⓒ 16 m

Ⓓ 18 m

30 The socks Jenny likes are priced at 3 pairs for $7. How many pairs of socks can she buy for $42?

Ⓐ 6   Ⓒ 15

Ⓑ 14   Ⓓ 18

31 Which figure has exactly one line of symmetry?

Ⓐ    Ⓒ

Ⓑ   Ⓓ

32 Carol bought 3 CDs that cost $12 each. She gave the clerk $50. How much change did she get back?

Ⓐ $36   Ⓒ $16

Ⓑ $24   Ⓓ $14

33 Which is an obtuse triangle?

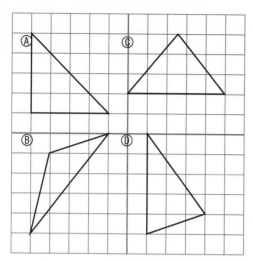

34 Which statement is true of both a parallelogram and a square?

Ⓐ Both have at least two right angles.

Ⓑ Both have opposite sides parallel.

Ⓒ Both have all angles equal.

Ⓓ Both have all sides the same length.

35 Which BEST describes two lines that meet at a right angle?

Ⓐ intersecting

Ⓑ vertical

Ⓒ parallel

Ⓓ perpendicular

36 Which quadrilateral has four right angles?

Ⓐ trapezoid

Ⓑ parallelogram

Ⓒ square

Ⓓ rhombus

Write an answer for each question.

---

37 Write 35,609 in expanded notation.

Answer: _____

38 Amy made this line plot of some kitten's weights.

Weights of Kittens

```
                        X
            X           X
   X        X    X      X
   X        X    X      X      X
 ─────────────────────────────────
  2 3/8    2 1/2  2 5/8  2 3/4  2 7/8
```

Weight (in Pounds)

What is the difference between the weight of the heaviest and the lightest kittens?

Answer: _____

39 Jordan got an order of 1,152 notepads for his store. They came in 8 boxes. How many notepads were in each box?

Answer: _____

40 What is the quotient?

$$900 \div 9 = \square$$

Answer: _____

41 Angle *TSQ* measures 123°. What is the measure of angle *RST*?

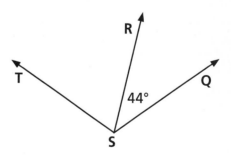

Answer: _____

GO ON

42 Marsha spent \$2,650 for a used car. Tony spent 4 times that amount for his used car. How much did Tony spend?

Answer: _____

43 How many hours are there in a 31-day month? (Remember there are 24 hours in a day.)

Answer: _____

44 How many 6-ounce servings can Sally make from 15 pounds of turkey? (Remember there are 16 ounces in a pound.)

Answer: _____

45 Write a fraction equivalent to $\frac{3}{10}$ that has a denominator of 100.

Answer: _____

46 Wesley spent \$93.25 last week. Judy spent \$92.90. Write $<$, $>$, or $=$ to compare the amounts they spent.

$93.25 \bigcirc \$92.90

47 Matt can walk 4 miles in an hour. How far can he walk in $\frac{3}{4}$ of an hour?

Answer: _____

48 Classify the angles and identify perpendicular and parallel sides to describe this quadrilateral. Classify the quadrilateral.

Answer: _____

_____

_____

49 Create a pattern that follows the rule "add 6."

Pattern: _____

Show all of your work. Explain in words the steps you follow.

Explanation: _____

_____

_____

_____

_____

_____

_____

GO ON

50 Find the measures of $\angle ABC$, $\angle CBD$, and $\angle ABD$.

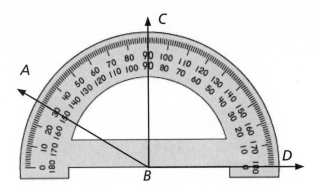

Answer: _____

Show OR describe each step of your work. Explain in writing each of your steps.

Explanation:_____

_____

_____

_____

_____

Points Earned/Total = _____ /50

Keeping Score

	Points Earned	Total Points	Percent Score
Tryout Test		/50	%
Test Practice 1 Number Sense		/20	%
Test Practice 2 Algebraic Thinking		/14	%
Test Practice 3 Whole Number Operations		/20	%
Test Practice 4 Fractions and Decimals		/20	%
Test Practice 5 Measurement and Data		/17	%
Test Practice 6 Geometry		/16	%
Mastery Test		/50	%

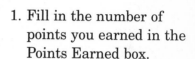

1. Fill in the number of points you earned in the Points Earned box.

2. Use the Finding Percent chart on page 110 to figure out your Percent Score. Then fill in the % box.

3. Compare your Percent Scores for the Tryout Test and the Mastery Test. See how much you've learned!

Finding Percent

Many tests give your score in both number of points earned and in percentages. This handy chart will tell you your percent score.

1. Find the band with the same number of points that are on your test.
2. Follow along the top row of the band to the number of points you earned. Your percent score is right below it.

Number of Points on Test

14

1	2	3	4	5	6	7	8	9	10	11	12	13	14
7%	14%	21%	29%	36%	43%	50%	57%	64%	71%	79%	86%	93%	100%

16

1	2	3	4	5	6	7	8	9	10	11	12	13	14	15	16
6%	13%	19%	25%	31%	38%	44%	50%	56%	63%	69%	75%	81%	88%	94%	100%

17

1	2	3	4	5	6	7	8	9	10	11	12	13	14	15	16	17
6%	12%	18%	24%	29%	35%	41%	47%	53%	59%	65%	71%	76%	82%	88%	94%	100%

20

1	2	3	4	5	6	7	8	9	10	11	12	13	14	15	16	17	18	19	20
5%	10%	15%	20%	25%	30%	35%	40%	45%	50%	55%	60%	65%	70%	75%	80%	85%	90%	95%	100%

50

1	2	3	4	5	6	7	8	9	10	11	12	13	14	15	16	17	18	19	20
2%	4%	6%	8%	10%	12%	14%	16%	18%	20%	22%	24%	26%	28%	30%	32%	34%	36%	38%	40%

21	22	23	24	25	26	27	28	29	30	31	32	33	34	35	36	37	38	39	40
42%	44%	46%	48%	50%	52%	54%	56%	58%	60%	62%	64%	66%	68%	70%	72%	74%	76%	78%	80%

41	42	43	44	45	46	47	48	49	50
82%	84%	86%	88%	90%	92%	94%	96%	98%	100%